CurriculumBa

KEY STAGE TWO
SCOTTISH LEVELS C-E

NUMBER

LYNETTE KELLY AND KATHY HALL

Published by Scholastic Limited,
Villiers House,
Clarendon Avenue,
Leamington Spa,
Warwickshire CV32 5PR
Text © Lynette Kelly and Kathy Hall
© 1995 Scholastic Limited
67890   8901234

AUTHORS
LYNETTE KELLY AND KATHY HALL

EDITOR
JO SAXELBY-JENNINGS

SERIES DESIGNER
LYNNE JOESBURY

DESIGNER
CLARE BREWER

ILLUSTRATIONS
RHIAN NEST-JAMES AND CHRIS ROTHEROE
(LINDEN ARTISTS)

COVER ILLUSTRATION
JONATHAN BENTLEY

INFORMATION TECHNOLOGY CONSULTANT
MARTIN BLOWS

SCOTTISH 5-14 LINKS
MARGARET SCOTT AND SUSAN GOW

Designed using Aldus Pagemaker

British Library Cataloguing-in-Publication Data
A catalogue record for this book is available from the British
Library.

ISBN 0-590-53382-7

Contents

ACKNOWLEDGEMENTS

The publishers wish to acknowledge the invaluable assistance and advice given by Shelagh Bird and Gill Perry in compiling this book.

Introduction

Scholastic Curriculum Bank is a series for all primary teachers, providing both an essential planning tool for devising comprehensive schemes of work as well as an easily accessible and varied bank of practical, classroom-tested activities with photocopiable resources.

Designed to help planning for and implementation of progression, differentiation and assessment, *Scholastic Curriculum Bank* offers a structured range of stimulating activities with clearly-stated learning objectives that reflect the programmes of study, and detailed lesson plans that allow busy teachers to put the ideas into practice with the minimum amount of preparation time. The photocopiable sheets that accompany many of the activities provide ways of integrating purposeful application of knowledge and skills, differentiation, assessment and record-keeping.

Opportunities for formative assessment are highlighted where appropriate within the activities, while separate summative assessment activities give guidelines for analysis and subsequent action. Ways of using information technology for different purposes and within different contexts, as a tool for communicating and handling information and as a method for investigating, are integrated into the activities where appropriate and more explicit guidance is provided at the end of the book.

The series covers all the primary curriculum subjects with separate books for Key Stages 1 and 2/Scottish Levels A–B and C–E. It can be used as a flexible resource with any scheme to fulfil National Curriculum and Scottish 5–14 requirements and to provide children with a variety of different learning experiences that will lead to effective acquisition of skills and knowledge.
numbers.

SCHOLASTIC CURRICULUM BANK MATHEMATICS

The *Scholastic Curriculum Bank Mathematics* books enable teachers to plan comprehensive and structured coverage of the primary mathematics curriculum and pupils to develop the required skills, knowledge and understanding through activities that promote mathematical thinking and ways of working.

There are two books for Key Stage 1/Scottish Levels A–B and two for Key Stage 2/Scottish Levels C–E reflecting the sections of the programmes of study:

▲ Number (including Handling Data);

▲ Shape, Space and Measures.

Using and Applying Mathematics is integrated into these contexts as required by the National Curriculum and these links are highlighted on the grid on pages 156–157.

Bank of activities

This book provides a bank of activities that can be used in many different ways – to form a framework for a scheme of work; to add breadth and variety to an existing scheme; to supplement a particular topic. The activities are designed to address a number of important areas of study.

Range

There is a range of activities provided, involving both first-hand experiences and the use of other sources of information. The activities allow pupils to develop mathematical language, select and use materials, and develop reasoning in the context of the areas of mathematics.

Opportunities for the use of calculators are provided for as a means to explore number and as a tool for calculating with realistic data.

The range of activities allows pupils to acquire the five elements of learning mathematics: facts, concepts, skills, strategies and attitudes.

▲ Facts are items of information which are unconnected and not supported by concepts, for example, a telephone number or postcode.

▲ Concepts are ideas growing continually in the mind. They become richly interconnected and form a network of understanding, for example, place value or subtraction.

▲ Skills are mental or physical procedures often involving several stages, for example, using a calculator.

▲ Strategies are procedures for choosing which skills and knowledge to use, for example, trial and improvement.

▲ Attitudes are developed in many ways. Positive attitudes to mathematics are necessary for future learning.

Communication skills

The activities aim to develop children's communication skills by encouraging them to:

▲ ask questions;

▲ explain their thinking;

▲ understand and use mathematical language;

▲ discuss their work;

▲ use a variety of forms of mathematical presentation;

▲ devise and refine their own ways of recording;

▲ present information and results clearly.

Mathematics in everyday life

Contexts used for the activities in these books have been chosen to be appropriate for the age of the pupils, familiar to their experience and relevant to their level of maturity.

Lesson plans

Detailed lesson plans, under clear headings, are given for each activity and provide teacher-ready material for immediate implementation in the classroom. The structure for each activity is as follows:

Activity title box

The information contained in the title box at the beginning of each activity outlines the following key aspects:

▲ *Activity title and learning objective:* For each activity there is a clearly stated learning objective which is given in bold italics. These learning objectives break down aspects of the programme of study into manageable, hierarchical, teaching and learning chunks, and their purpose is to aid planning for progression. These objectives can be easily referenced to the National Curriculum and Scottish 5–14 requirements by using the overview grids at the end of this introduction (pages 9–12).

▲ *Class organisation/Likely duration:* Icons ✝✝ and 🕐 signpost the suggested group sizes for each activity and the approximate amount of time required to complete it.

Previous skills/knowledge needed
Information is given here when it is necessary for the children to have acquired specific knowledge or skills prior to carrying out the activity.

Key background information
The information given in this section is intended to support teachers' subject knowledge of mathematics and to show how the mathematics is incorporated into the activity where necessary.

Preparation
Advice is given for those occasions where it is necessary for the teacher to orientate the pupils to the activity or to prepare materials, or set up a display or activity ahead of time.

Resources needed
All the materials needed to carry out the activity are listed so that either pupils or teacher can gather them together easily before the beginning of the teaching session.

What to do
Easy to follow, step-by-step instructions are given for carrying out the activity including, where appropriate, suggested questions for the teacher to ask the pupils to help instigate discussion and stimulate investigation.

Suggestion(s) for extension/support
Wherever feasible, the activities lend themselves to easy differentiation. In all cases, suggestions are provided as to how each activity can be modified for the less able or extended for the more able.

Assessment opportunities
Each activity has clearly staged assessment opportunities which relate directly to the learning objectives for that activity and provide the framework for ongoing assessment. By taking advantage of these assessment opportunities teachers can reassure themselves that the stated learning objectives have been achieved. This important knowledge will ensure that teachers are sufficiently informed about children's learning and progress to be able to plan a curriculum and learning experiences that meet their present learning needs

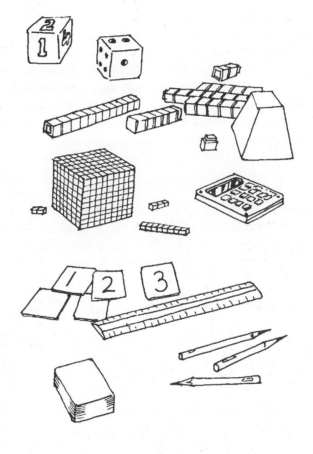

and supports future progress within the mathematics curriculum.

Opportunities for IT
Where opportunities for IT present themselves, these are briefly outlined with reference to particularly suitable types of program. The chart on page 159 presents specific areas of IT covered in the activities together with more detailed support on how to apply particular types of program. Selected lesson plans serve as models for other activities by providing more comprehensive guidance on the application of IT and these are indicated by the bold page numbers on the grid and the ▫ icon at the start of an activity.

Display ideas
Where relevant, display ideas are incorporated into activity plans and illustrated with examples.

Reference to photocopiable sheets
Where activities include photocopiable worksheets, small reproductions of these are included in the lesson plans together with guidance notes for their use, and, where appropriate, suggested answers.

Assessment
There will be key points in time when teachers wish to take an overview of each pupil's achievement in mathematics. Consequently this chapter provides a number of specific assessment activities related to the main areas of study covered elsewhere in the book that can be used for formative and/or summative assessment purposes. These activities provide focused assessment opportunities across a range of interrelated learning objectives which will form the basis, alongside other types of evidence, for the major summative assessment at the end of the key stage against the level descriptions. In these lesson plans guidance is given for what to look for from the pupils and what that might mean for their future learning of mathematics.

Using and applying mathematics
Aspects of using and applying mathematics are integral to each activity. Using and applying mathematics cannot be

taught separately from the other areas of mathematics. It cannot exist alone. It must be set in the context of mathematical content. It should be thought of more as a teaching methodology and a mathematical process than as a distinct and separate content area. The teaching methodology relies strongly on the ability to challenge pupils through questioning and extending tasks. Pupils need to be encouraged to ask questions and follow alternative suggestions to support the development of reasoning. Therefore, on pages 156–157 a grid relating each activity to using and applying mathematics is provided. This grid will enable teachers to ensure that sufficient time and attention is paid to this central area of mathematics.

Photocopiable sheets

Many of the activities are accompanied by photocopiable sheets. For some activities, there may be more than one version of a worksheet suggested, or a sheet will be 'generic' with a facility for the teacher to fill in the appropriate task in order to provide differentiation by task. Other sheets may be more open-ended to provide differentiation by outcome. The photocopiable sheets provide purposeful activities that are ideal for assessment and for keeping as records in pupils' portfolios of work.

Cross-curricular links

Cross-curricular links are identified on a simple grid on page 160 cross-referencing particular areas of study in mathematics to the programmes of study for other subjects.

NUMBER AT KEY STAGE 2

This book covers the development of number at Key Stage 2 as outlined in the programmes of study for Number and Handling Data.

The range of skills and concepts involved in the development of number have been summarised in the National Curriculum as follows:

▲ developing an understanding of place value and extending the number system;

▲ understanding relationships between numbers and developing methods of computation;

▲ solving numerical problems;

▲ developing flexible methods of computation and recording;

▲ using calculators and computers to explore number structure and work with realistic data;

▲ developing the skills needed for accurate and appropriate use of equipment.

The structure of this book reflects the detailed requirements set out in the programme of study for Number. It is divided into four main sections:

▲ Number structure – in which the activities concern place value, including decimals and fractions;

▲ Number relationships – in which the activities concern patterns, number facts and special numbers;

▲ Calculations – in which the activities concern operations, problems and checking;

▲ Handling data – in which the activities concern the representation of data, and probability.

Learning objective	PoS/AO	Content	Type of activity	Page
Number structure – *Place value, rounding, negative and decimal numbers*				
To be able to create the largest or smallest three-digit number possible from three given digits.	N 2a *NMM: Range and type of numbers, Level B*	Placing digits in order of size to make the highest possible number.	Small group.	14
To be able to develop a strategy for creating the largest possible addition sum from three, four or five given	Number 2a *NMM: Range and type of numbers, Level C*	Making addition sums from three, four or five given digits.	Large group, then pairs.	15
To be able to multiply and divide one-, two- and three-digit numbers by 10 and 100.	N 2a *NMM: Multiply and divide, Level C*	Multiplying and dividing by 10 and 100 using a calculator.	Large group.	16
To be able to round numbers to the nearest 10 confidently and accurately.	N 2a *NMM: Round numbers, Level B*	Rounding numbers to 10.	Large group, then pairs.	17
To be able to use knowledge of rounding to approximate answers to calculations involving two- and three-digit numbers.	N 4c *NMM: Round numbers, Level C*	Calculating approximate answers to sums.	Large group, then individuals, then pairs.	18
To begin to develop an understanding of negative numbers.	N 2b *NMM: Range and type of numbers, Level E*	Exploring negative numbers on a number line.	Small group, then pairs.	19
To be able to use decimal notation in money accurately.	N 2b *NMM: Range and type of numbers, Level C*	Calculating prices using decimal notation.	Pairs or individuals.	21
Number structure – *Fractions*				
To be able to read fraction notation. To recognise simple fractions as part of a unit. To recognise equivalence of simple fractions.	N 2c *NMM: Fractions, percentages and ratio, Level B*	Collecting fraction pieces according to the throw of a dice.	Pairs.	22
To be able to identify simple equivalent fractions.	N 2c *NMM: Range and type of numbers, Level C*	Finding equivalent fractions.	Individuals.	22
To be able to order simple mixed numbers. To be able to understand the notation of mixed numbers.	N 2c *NMM: Range and type of numbers, Level D*	Ordering mixed numbers.	Small group or pairs, then whole class.	23
To be able to use and apply knowledge of fractions to find an answer. To use mathematical reasoning and knowledge to find an answer.	N 2c *NMM: Fractions, percentages and ratio, Level E*	Using clues involving fractions to identify 'missing' numbers.	Large group. then pairs.	24
To begin to relate the equivalence of simple fractions and percentages.	N 2c *NMM: Fractions, percentages and ratio, Level D*	Describing proportions using fractions and percentages.	Individuals.	25
To understand that a percentage means 'out of 100'. To be able to recognise the equivalence of fractions (hundredths) and percentages.	N 2c *NMM: Fractions, percentages and ratio, Level E*	Calculating the percentage equivalent to a fraction.	Individuals.	26
Number relationships – *Patterns*				
To recognise and explain patterns of multiples. To recognise relationships between sets of multiples.	N 3a *NMM: Patterns and sequences, Level C*	Exploring patterns and relationships between sets of multiples using a 100 square.	Large group.	28
To be able to recognise a number pattern and use square numbers.	N 3a *NMM: Patterns and sequences, Level E*	Finding squares in different-sized square grids.	Large group, then individuals.	29
To look at patterns in magic squares.	N 3a *NMM: Patterns and sequences, Level C*	Identifying 3 × 3 magic squares and generating new squares.	Individuals or small group.	31
To introduce the pattern of numbers known as 'Pascal's triangle'. To explore patterns of numbers within the triangle.	N 3a *NMM: Patterns and sequences, Level E*	Building 'Pascal's triangle' and exploring patterns within it.	Large group, then individuals.	32

NUMBER

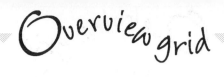

Learning objective	PoS/AO	Content	Type of activity	Page
To use knowledge of properties of numbers to find relationships between two numbers.	N 3a *NMM: Patterns and sequences, Level C*	Establish relationships between two numbers.	Small group.	33

Number relationships – *Number facts*

Learning objective	PoS/AO	Content	Type of activity	Page
To be able to use knowledge of addition and subtraction facts.	N 3c *NMM: Add and subtract, Level B*	Using addition and subtraction facts to play a game.	Pairs.	34
To be able to recall knowledge of addition facts to complete addition grids.	N 3c *NMM: Add and subtract, Levels B and C*	Completing addition squares.	Individuals, then pairs.	35
To be able to recall number facts using addition and subtraction.	N 3c *NMM: Add and subtract, Level C*	Answering addition and subtraction questions to fill in number puzzles.	Individuals.	37
To make a multiplication square and explore the patterns within it. To be able to recall multiplication facts to 10 × 10.	N 3c *NMM: Multiply and divide, Level C*	Compiling and using a 10 × 10 multiplication square.	Individuals.	38
To be able to use multiplication facts to 10 × 10.	N 3c *NMM: Multiply and divide, Level C*	Deciphering a number code based on multiplication.	Individuals.	39
To recall number facts involving multiplication and division. To use the relationshipo between multiplication and division.	N 3c *NMM: Multiply and divide, Level C*	Using division and multiplication facts to follow a pathway.	Individuals.	40
To combine sets of numbers to make 20. To use knowledge of number facts to 20 to add a string of numbers.	N 3c *NMM: Add and subtract, Level B*	Finding combinations of numbers which add up to 20.	Whole class, then pairs, then whole class.	41
To be able to see the pattern when adding multiples of 10 to any number and to add mentally multiples of 10 to any number.	N 3c *NMM: Add and subtract, Level C*	Adding 10 and its multiples to different methods.	Small group.	42
To be able to add 9 and 99 to a number quickly. To be able to subtract 9 and 99 from a number quickly.	N 3c *NMM: Add and subtract, Level C*	Adding and subtracting 9 and 99.	Large group, then pairs.	44

Number relationships – *Special numbers*

Learning objective	PoS/AO	Content	Type of activity	Page
To be able to identify factors of numbers to 40. To look at the total number of factors of particular numbers.	N 3c *NMM: Multiply and divide, Level C*	Finding factors of numbers.	Pairs.	45
To be able to break down a number into its factors, using multiplication facts.	N 3c *NMM: Multiply and divide, Levels C and E*	Build factor trees to find prime factors.	Small group.	47
To recognise and investigate 'Fibonacci Numbers'.	N 3c *NMM: Patterns and sequences, Level D*	Introducing 'Fibonacci Numbers'.	Pairs.	48
To be able to identify prime numbers below 100, using the 'Sieve of Eratosthenes'.	N 3c *NMM: Patterns and sequences, Level E*	Using 'Sieve of Eratosthenes' to identify and explore prime numbers.	Whole class or individuals, then whole class or large group.	50
To use and recognise index notation, including numbers to the power 2 and 3, and to be able to identify cube numbers.	N 3c *NMM: Multiply and divide, Level D*	Using index and notation for square and cube numbers.	Small group.	51
To identify numbers by discovering their properties. To use knowledge of primes, multiples, factors, square, rectangular and cube numbers.	N 3c *NMM: Patterns and sequences, Level E*	Answering questions about numbers less than 50.	Small group.	53

Calculations – *Operations*

Learning objective	PoS/AO	Content	Type of activity	Page
To be able to subtract two-digit numbers mentally by counting on.	N 3d *NMM: Add and subtract/ Multiply and divide, Level B*	Counting on to reach a target number.	Individuals.	56
To be able to use the four operations confidently. To be able to apply the inverse of an operation.	N 3f *NMM: Add and subtract/ Multiply and divide, Level B*	Using all four operations to reach a target number.	Individuals.	57

NUMBER

Learning objective	PoS/AO	Content	Type of activity	Page
To be able to calculate a simple fraction of an amount using a calculator.	N 3g *NMM: Fractions, percentages and ratio, Level B*	Game, using 100 square, calculating fractions of numbers.	Pairs.	58
To be able to calculate a simple percentage of an amount using a calculator.	N 3g *NMM: Fractions, percentages and ratio, Level E*	Calculating the sale price of various articles reduced by 10%, 50% and 25%.	Small group.	60
To be able to add and subtract with decimals to two decimal places.	N 3g *NMM: Add and subtract, Level D*	Game involving addition and subtraction of decimals.	Pairs.	61
To be able to add and subtract decimals to two places.	N 3g *NMM: Add and subtract, Level D*	Game involving addition and subtraction of decimals.	Pairs.	63

Calculations – *Problems*

Learning objective	PoS/AO	Content	Type of activity	Page
To be able to use mathematical reasoning and knowledge to find an answer.	N 4a *NMM: Add and subtract/ Multiply and divide, Level C*	Discovering a number from a set of clues.	Individuals.	64
To be able to solve simple problems using addition.	N 4a *NMM: Patterns and sequences, Level B*	Combining numbers to make different totals.	Small group.	65
To be able to calculate percentage parts of quantities.	N 4b *NMM: Fractions, percentages and ratio, Level E*	Calculating the percentage of children in school today.	Small group.	66
To be able to choose appropriate mathematical operation to solve a problem. To be able to increase a recipe in proportion.	N 4b *NMM: Fractions, percentages and ratio, Level E*	Increasing a recipe in proportion.	Small group.	67
To be able to use a calculator to solve a problem. To know which operation to apply in solving a practical money problem. To be able to calculate the cost of a single item using the concept of proportion.	N 4a *NMM: Fractions, percentages and ratio, Level E*	Calculating the cost of one biscuit from a recipe for 20.	Small group.	68
To be able to combine prices up to £100.	N 4a *NMM: Add and subtract, Level D*	Deciding how to spend £100 towards equipping a school cookery room.	Small group.	70
To be able to solve problems involving addition of amounts of money.	N 4a *NMM: Add and subtract/ Multiply and divide, Level E*	Calculating the cost of a day trip for the class.	Individuals.	71

Calculations – *Checking*

Learning objective	PoS/AO	Content	Type of activity	Page
To be able to estimate and approximate solutions to division problems.	N 4c *NMM: Round numbers, Level D*	Game involving identifying a missing number in multiplication and division sentences.	Pairs.	71
To be able to check results using inverse operations.	N 4c *NMM: Functions and equations, Level E*	Discovering 'rules' used to generate numbers.	Individuals.	73
To be able to check addition through adding a set of data in a different order.	N 4c *NMM: Add and subtract, Level D*	Adding list of numbers in a different order.	Large group.	74
To be able to check addition through the use of subtraction.	N 4c *NMM: Add and subtract, Level C*	Adding a list of numbers and checking total by reversing the process.	Pairs.	75
To be able to cross-check by adding numbers in a different order.	N 4c *NMM: Add and subtract, Level B*	Using cross-checking to solve puzzles such as arithmagons.	Individuals (or pairs).	76

NUMBER

Learning objective	PoS/AO	Content	Type of activity	Page
To be able to check calculations by using inverse operations.	N 4c *NMM: Add and subtract/ Multiply and divide, Level B*	Calculator game, to discover partner's hidden number.	Pairs.	78
Handling Data – *Handling data*				
To be able to set up and explore a database on the computer. To search for and find information on a computer database. To be able to list information from a computer database. To be able to sort information on a computer database. To be able to do a print-out of information.	HD 1c *IH: Collect/Organise, Level D*	Children use computer to input data they have already collected through questionnaires. They then access data from the database.	Small group activity at computer.	80
To be able to present data in a bar graph. To recognise that the same information can be presented in different ways. To be able to interpret data presented in a bar graph. To be able to compare bar graphs showing the same data from different groups.	HD 2b *IH: Display/Interpret, Level C*	Children present data on favourite pop groups on a bar chart. They compare data from another class by presenting and comparing two bar graphs.	Large group or whole class.	82
To be able to interpret data presented in a bar chart using different scales on one of the axes. To recognise that the same information can be presented in different ways, using different scales.	HD 2b *IH: Display/Interpret, Level C*	Children access information on favourite TV programmes from the database and graph this using a simple scale.	Whole class or large group.	84
To be able to present data on a line graph. To recognise that the same information can be presented in different ways by switching the information on the horizontal and vertical axes. To recognise that the same information can be presented in different ways, using different scales.	HD 2b *IH: Display/Interpret, Level D*	Children present (experimental?) data using a line graph.	Whole class or large group, then individuals or pairs.	85
To understand, calculate and use the mean of a set of data. To understand, calculate and use the range of a set of data.	HD 2c *IH: Interpret, Level E*	Children use calculators to calculate the mean number of brothers and sisters of people in the class. They are introduced to the notion of spread – the range.	Whole class or large group, then pairs.	87
Handling Data – *Probability*				
To recognise that the probability of any event lies between impossibility and certainty. To understand and use correctly some basic probability terminology: impossible, very unlikely, unlikely, likely, very likely and certain. To be able to order these terms according to the degree of probability. To be able to use a probability scale to estimate, compare and justify likelihood.	HD 3a and 3b *IH: beyond Level E*	Children apply the language of possibility to experiences in their own lives and to hypothetical situations.	Whole class or large group .	89
To recognise and use the concept of 'evens' and 'even chance'. To recognise that an event has one or more possible outcomes. To list the possible outcomes of an event. To be able to predict outcomes where there are two possibilities.	HD 3b and 3c *IH: beyond Level E*	Children experiment with tossing coins and are introduced to the concept of evens and even chance. On the basis of experimenting, they predict outcomes.	Large group or whole class, then pairs, then large group or whole class.	90
To be able to distinguish between 'fair' and 'unfair'. To be able to place events in order of likelihood. To recognise that different outcomes may result from repeating an experiment.	HD 3a, 3b and 3c *IH: beyond Level E*	Through constructing spinners of different types and playing games the children decide on what counts as a fair game and on calculating probability.	Group of four.	92

On this planning grid the following code is applied: N = Number PoS, HD = Handling data PoS; (Scottish 5–14 Guidelines references are given in italic type)
NMM = Number, money and measurement AO, *IH* = Information handling AO.

Number structure

Developing an understanding of the structure of our number system and how it works is a crucial part of the learning of mathematics. Children need to develop a feel for number and know about the relative si~~~ ~~ ~~~~bers. They need opportunities to develop skills of estimation and approximation in order to judge whether the answer to a calculation or problem is reasonable or not. Understanding and exploring our number structure involves not only whole numbers, but also negative numbers, decimals and fractional numbers.

Very often further numerical process in the primary school and beyond is hindered by an inadequate understanding of place value. Children require plenty of practical activities, discussion and opportunities to explore the number system in order to ensure an adequate grasp of the structure of number.

Fractions are used throughout everyday life, especially simple fractions such as halves, quarters and three-quarters. Percentages are frequently used to present information on television, radio and in newspapers too. Children need to be able to understand these terms and interpret their meaning.

There are two sections in this chapter. The first (pages 14–21) deals with place value, rounding and approximation and the understanding and use of negative and decimal numbers. The second section (pages 22–26) deals with fractions, progressing from the recognition of simple equivalent fractions to using percentages to describe and compare data.

BIG, BIGGER, BIGGEST

To be able to create the largest or smallest three-digit number possible from three given digits.

†† *Group of two to six children.*

🕐 *30–45 minutes.*

Previous skills/knowledge needed

To be able to read, write and recognise numbers up to 100 and to have a developing understanding that the position of a digit signifies its value.

Key background information

A central feature of our place value system is that the digits representing the larger groupings appear to the left when recording particular numbers. Position or *place* is important. It is vital that the children have plenty of practice in associating the written number and the position of the digits with the relative size of the number.

Preparation

Give the children the opportunity to explore putting numbers up to 100 in order of size. Encourage them to use the language greatest, greater, smallest, smaller, highest, higher, lowest and lower accurately and confidently.

Make two sets of 0–9 number cards for each group by copying photocopiable sheet 106 the required number of times and then cutting up the pages into individual cards. You will also need to make a copy of sheet 107 for each child.

Resources needed

Two sets of 0–9 number cards per group, a large sheet of paper, marker pen, paper, pencils, a copy of photocopiable worksheet 107 for each child, 0–100 number lines or base 10 equipment (optional).

What to do

Show two sets of the number cards to the children. Shuffle the cards together and place them face down. Pick up the top two cards and show them to the children. Ask the children how they think you can arrange the cards to give the highest number that can be made. Pick another card and lay the three cards you have picked face up on the table. Ask the children to give you all the possible alternative three-digit numbers which can be made from the cards. You could write their suggestions on a large sheet of paper. Repeat this process a few times so that the children get the idea of rearranging the digit cards.

Give each child a copy of photocopiable sheet 107 and tell them that they are going to play a game using the cards and the sheets they have just been given. Someone will need to keep a record of the score.

Explain the rules of the game. In turn, each child picks and keeps a card from the shuffled pack. As a card is picked the player has to decide in which column (using box 1 on the sheet) to write that particular digit – either the units, tens, or hundreds column. This should be done before the next player takes a card. When everyone has had three turns, each player reads aloud his number. The player with the highest number is the winner of that round. The cards are collected, reshuffled and the game begins again.

Suggestion(s) for extension

As the children play the game, encourage them to take note of which cards have been picked up by other players and to assess their own chances of choosing a higher or lower card.

The game can be played using four- or five-digit numbers, with the number of cards increased accordingly.

A variation of the game could be played where the winner is the player who makes the lowest number or the number nearest to 500.

Suggestion(s) for support

Work closely with the children, initially playing the game using just two digits. Encourage them to represent their numbers using base 10 equipment to compare the two possible alternatives. Alternatively they could mark the two numbers on a number line and see which is nearer to 100.

Assessment opportunities

When the ten rounds of the game are over, ask the children to look back over their game sheets and, in the spaces provided, write the highest (or lowest) numbers that they could have made with their three digits each time.

Ask the children each to choose one of their games and write out *all* the possible three-digit numbers they could have made, placing them in order from highest to lowest.

These tasks will help you to know how well the children have grasped the idea that rearranging the digits alters the value of a number, and if they can order three-digit numbers according to size.

Display ideas

Ask the children to research in newspapers and the school library for the largest numbers they can find. A display of some of these numbers, placed in order of size and labelled with their value in words, can then be created.

Reference to photocopiable sheets

Photocopiable sheet 106 is used to make 0–9 digit cards. Two copies will be needed for each group. Digit cards are a resource that is used for many of the activities in this book and so you may wish to copy or stick the numbers on to card and laminate or cover them with clear adhesive plastic to prolong their life.

Photocopiable sheet 107 is a record sheet and one copy will be required for each child.

Resources needed

A copy of the photocopiable worksheet on page 108 for each child, paper, pencils, calculators (optional).

What to do

Explain to the children that you want them to work on a problem which will involve them in finding the largest possible number as the answer. Start by writing down three numbers: say, 1, 3 and 7. Ask the children to find the largest addition sum they can using each of these three numbers only once. Give them an example: 13 + 7 = 20. Can they think of any more?

Set the children working on the problem. After a short while, discuss their answers with them. Then ask them to try the same problem, but using three different numbers. Give each pair of children a copy of the worksheet (photocopiable sheet 108). Ask them to use the sheet to record their work.

Leave the children to work in their pairs, suggesting they try different combinations of the digits. Ask them if they can discover any rules. Ask questions such as: What is the highest digit of the three? Where does this digit end up; as a unit or a ten? Does it make any difference where the other two digits are placed? Try to get the children to predict the largest addition sum they can make before they do the calculation.

Using just three digits will be fairly straightforward for many children, and they should complete this task relatively quickly. If they do, ask them to try using four and five digits. They will need another copy of photocopiable worksheet 108 for each attempt. Leave them to investigate their findings. At the end of the lesson, draw the class together to discuss the work and any conclusions they may have drawn.

THE GREATEST ANSWER

To be able to develop a strategy for creating the largest possible addition sum from three, four and five digits.

†† *Large group, then pairs.*

🕑 *30–45 minutes.*

Previous skills/knowledge needed

The children should be familiar with whole numbers up to 1000 and the addition of two-digit and three-digit numbers.

Key background information

This activity stresses the importance of the place of digits in signifying their value and will help the children's understanding of the structure of our number system, its place value and notation.

Preparation

Give the children the opportunity to explore ordering numbers to 1000 by size. Encourage the accurate use of the appropriate language. Photocopy worksheet 108 for each pair. Copy a few spare sheets for the extension work.

Suggestion(s) for extension

Using further copies of photocopiable worksheet 108, some children may be keen to investigate all possible combinations using three, four or five digits. If so, ask them to use the digits to find the addition sum with the smallest answer. A further extension would be to find the highest product using a certain amount of digits. For example, with the digits 2, 6, 4 and 1 they could try 26 × 41, 24 × 16, 64 × 12, 146 × 2 and so on. Using calculators will free the children to concentrate on prediction rather than working randomly through all the possible combinations. This could be tried using five digits also.

Suggestions for support
Provide the three digits with which the children should work. Encourage them to try all the possible combinations first, before trying to come up with any special rule.

Assessment opportunities
Observe the children's approach to the activity and, through discussion, identify whether they are able to develop an appropriate strategy and predict the combination that will provide the largest answer.

Display ideas
The children's discoveries could be displayed alongside the strategy they used, written by the children in their own words.

Reference to photocopiable sheet
Photocopiable sheet 108 is a record sheet which the children can fill in as they complete the activity. Further copies of the sheet can be used by the children for the extension activities.

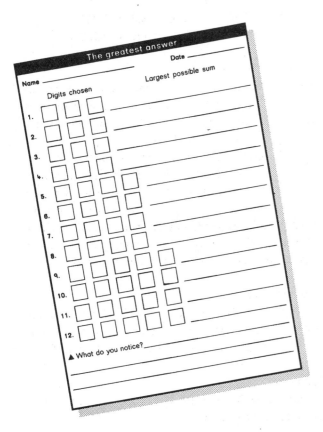

MOVING DIGITS

To be able to multiply and divide one-, two- and three-digit numbers by 10 and 100.

†† *Large group.*

🕐 *30 minutes.*

Previous skills/knowledge needed
The children should be confident with place value and have an understanding of the operations of multiplication and division. They should also be able to use a basic calculator.

Key background information
It is important that the children see the process of multiplying by 10 or by 100 as the movement of digits one (or two) places to the left, rather than simply as adding zero(s). Additional activities using Multibase materials and place value boards will help the children exercise this movement.

Preparation
Using their calculators, ask the children to enter the number 4 and multiply it by 10 and then by 10 again. Ask them to try this with another digit. What do they notice? Ask them to predict what would happen if they did the same with a two-digit number. What do they think would happen if they multiply a number by 100. Let them try. What do they notice?

Encourage the children to record their answers. For example:

$$4 \times 10 = 40$$
$$40 \times 10 = 400$$
$$400 \times 10 = 4000$$

Now ask them to divide their results by 10. Start with 4000. What happens? Ask them to explore other starter numbers and explain their results.

In this activity, the children will come across decimal amounts. You may prefer to explain these beforehand in terms of money or measures.

Resources needed
Calculators, pencils, ruled paper, large cube as a dice marked with ×10, ÷10, ×1, ÷1, ×100, ÷100.

What to do
Give each child a piece of ruled paper, a pencil and a calculator. Ask the children to suggest a starting number, initially between 0 and 9. Tell them all to enter this number into their calculators. Now throw the dice and read the result aloud. The children should complete the calculation on their calculators. For example:

Starting number		5
Dice	×10	50

Ask the children to record the display on their calculator at the top of their piece of paper. Tell them to keep going, making a list of numbers down the paper, until the dice has been thrown ten times. Ask the children what their calculators show. Discuss the results.

Tell the children to start again to make a new list, but this time use a starting number consisting of two digits, for example, 23. Repeat the same process as before, throwing the dice ten times.

Now ask the children to repeat the activity but using a three-digit starting number.

Suggestion(s) for extension
Using a calculator the children can explore the division and multiplication of numbers by 0.1 and 0.01.

Suggestion(s) for support
Some children will find it easier to investigate the 10 times table supported by the use of base 10 materials.

Assessment opportunities
Ask the children to choose a starting number each and to keep it secret in their heads. Then ask them to multiply it by 10, divide it by 1, multiply it by 10 again and divide it by 100. What do they get? It should be their starting number!

If the children are reasonably confident with multiplying/ dividing by 10 and 100, they will not find this type of arithmetical mental 'gymnastics' daunting or complex.

Opportunities for IT
The children should be introduced to the fact that the calculator models the tens number system which accurately represents what happens when multiplying or dividing by 10. Although the children are unable to vary the rules of this model (as it is programmed into the calculator's control chip), they can vary the inputs and observe what happens to the output on the display. The children could be encouraged to predict what will be the result of multiplying by 100. Older or more-able children might like to experiment with some of the calculators that are provided free with many computers. In some of these it is possible to work in base 2 (binary) or base 16 (hexadecimal), where the calculator follows a different set of rules to make it work.

HOW HIGH CAN YOU GO?

To be able to round numbers to the nearest 10 confidently and accurately.

†† *Large group, then pairs.*

🕐 *30 minutes.*

Previous skills/knowledge needed
The children should be familiar with the addition of two- and three-digit numbers and be able to use a basic calculator.

Key background information
The ability to round numbers to the nearest 10 or 100 allows children to develop skills of approximation and estimation. These skills are especially relevant when using a calculator. Mistakes can be made by accidentally pressing the wrong keys and will often go unnoticed if the children do not form the habit of estimating and then checking for 'sensible' answers.

The children will need to be taught the standard procedure for rounding numbers. For example:

▲ Rounding to the nearest 10
      61 – 64 (inclusive) rounds to 60
      65 – 69 (inclusive) rounds to 70
▲ Rounding to the nearest 100
      401 – 449 (inclusive) rounds to 400
      450 – 499 (inclusive) rounds to 500
▲ Rounding to the nearest 1000
      2001 – 2499 (inclusive) rounds to 2000
      2500 – 2999 (inclusive) rounds to 3000

Preparation
Discuss with the children the importance of estimation and being able to tell whether an answer to a calculation is sensible or not. Relate the ability to estimate and approximate to counting and measuring activities.

You will need to make two sets of 1–9 number cards for each pair of children. Make sufficient copies of photocopiable sheet 106 and then cut them into individual cards. Copying or mounting them on to card and/or laminating or covering them with clear sticky plastic will prolong their life. The children will also need a sheet of lined paper, preferably ruled with two vertical columns on each side (as shown on the next page).

Resources needed
For each pair you will need: two packs of 1–9 number cards (made from photocopiable sheet 106), a sheet of lined paper, pencils, calculator and/or 0–100 number line (optional).

What to do
Introduce the children to the idea of 'rounding' numbers up or down to the nearest 10.

Explain the standard procedure for rounding given on the previous page:

> *Under half-way, round down.*
> *Half-way and over, round up.*

Give each pair of children a set of cards and a sheet of lined paper between them. Ask them to shuffle the cards and spread them out so that they are face down on the table. Each player then turns over two cards to make a two-digit number. The children should then round this number to the nearest 10 and record both numbers on the lined paper (as shown above). The cards are then picked up and reshuffled and spread out again face down on the table. Again the players pick two cards in turn. This process is repeated for each round of the game. The children should add both columns of numbers using a calculator and compare the two totals. The player whose *rounded* numbers add up to the highest total is the winner.

Suggestion(s) for extension
Encourage the children to keep a running total of their scores. For rounding to the nearest 100, three cards can be picked.

Suggestion(s) for support
Ask the children to mark their two-digit numbers on the number line. This will help them to see if the numbers are to be rounded up or down.

Assessment opportunities
Observe the children as they participate in the activity. As they gain more practice, they should become quicker and more confident at rounding the numbers. Check if they understand the procedure for rounding numbers ending in 5, for example 45 would be rounded up to 50.

Opportunities for IT
The children's use of calculators should be considered a part of their IT development. They should be encouraged to look at their answers and check them for accuracy, relating the result to the expected answer and the keys pressed. As with computers, calculators depend on accurate keying and the correct sequences of commands to create accurate results.

Display ideas
The children could collect large numbers, for example, the attendances at football matches, which can then be rounded to the nearest 10, 100 and 1000. This information could be displayed by the children, perhaps as part of an overall display about 'Large numbers'.

Reference to photocopiable sheet
Copies of photocopiable sheet 106 are used to make the 1–9 number cards needed for this activity.

APPROXIMATING

To be able to use knowledge of rounding to approximate answers to calculations involving two- and three-digit numbers.

†† *Large group, then individuals, then pairs.*

🕐 *45 minutes.*

Previous skills/knowledge needed
The children should be able to use the four operations and should be able to round to the nearest 10 and 100. They should also be able to use a basic calculator.

Key background information
The standard procedure for rounding numbers is:

▲ Rounding to the nearest 10
> 61 – 64 (inclusive) rounds to 60
> 65 – 69 (inclusive) rounds to 70

▲ Rounding to the nearest 100
> 401 – 449 (inclusive) rounds to 400
> 450 – 499 (inclusive) rounds to 500

▲ Rounding to the nearest 1000
> 2001 – 2499 (inclusive) rounds to 2000
> 2500 – 2999 (inclusive) rounds to 3000

Preparation
The children should be confident with rounding numbers and should be able to use approximate numbers to estimate the

size of a solution. This will largely depend upon how confident they are with the four operations. It would be helpful for the children to revise together a number of examples of each operation, both with and without using a calculator.

Resources needed
A copy of each of the photocopiable sheets 109 and 110 for each child, pencils, paper, calculators.

What to do
In a large group, remind the children about the procedures for rounding to the nearest 10 and 100 (see 'Key background information'). Ask them to predict the method to be used for rounding to the nearest 1000.

Ask the children to suggest an addition sum involving two two-digit numbers, for example 73 and 19. Ask them to estimate the answer without working it out exactly. Now try a three-digit number addition, for example 237 + 684. Discuss together the approximate answers the children have found and the degree of accuracy possible. When do they think that it may be important to be more accurate? When do they think a less accurate approximation would be sufficient? For example, if you went shopping with only a little money you would need to estimate your bill quite accurately before going to the check-out. However, shopping with plenty of money you may need only a rough estimate of your bill before going to the check-out. Discuss rounding the above examples (237 + 684) to varying degrees of accuracy:

▲ 240 + 690 is approximately 930 to the nearest 10;
▲ or, 200 + 700 is approximately 900 to the nearest 100.

Now ask the children to complete photocopiable worksheets 109 and 110. The first sheet concentrates on approximating answers to addition and subtraction problems, while the second involves multiplication. When they have finished, ask them to work in pairs to discuss their answers.

Finally, encourage the children to create some calculations of their own and then try them out on their partners.

Suggestion(s) for extension
Devise other examples based on those provided, making the calculations more difficult, for example 320 + 461 + 782 or 600 × 30, 1040 × 20, and so on.

Suggestion(s) for support
Devise other examples based on those provided, making the calculations easier, for example 33 + 41, 78 + 34, 37 − 26, 44 − 28 and so on.

Assessment opportunities
Observe the children at work and assess their confidence with approximating solutions. Mark their answers on

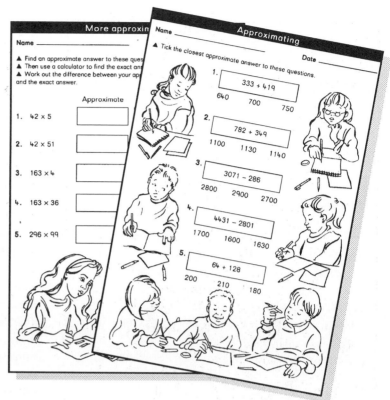

photocopiable sheets 109 and 110. Check to see whether they have made any errors consistently that might reveal a misunderstanding or misapplication of the rounding procedures.

Display ideas
Use the children's work as part of a classroom display.

Reference to photocopiable sheets
Photocopiable sheets 109 and 110 are both stimulus and recording sheets for the children to work from individually. The answers to sheet 109 are: **1.** 750; **2.** 1130; **3.** 2800; **4.** 1630; **5.** 200. The answers to sheet 110 are: **1.** 210; **2.** 2142; **3.** 652; **4.** 5868; **5.** 29304.

NEGATIVE NUMBERS

To begin to develop an understanding of negative numbers.

†† *Small groups, then pairs.*

⏱ *30 minutes.*

Previous skills/knowledge needed
The children should be familiar with using number lines.

Key background information
The children will have come across negative numbers in a variety of situations, both inside and outside school. A thermometer kept in the refrigerator or outside on the school building may have provided them with a visual representation

of temperatures below and above freezing point. They will have heard these terms used on the television or radio during weather forecasts. Also work in history may have introduced the idea of dates being known in terms of BC and AD. These, along with other examples, will illustrate that sometimes we need to measure in two opposite directions from a starting point. Any numerical quantity that may be negative or positive is called a 'directed number'. Games using a number line are a useful introduction to directed numbers.

Preparation

It will be useful to find out how much the children already know about negative numbers. As well as discussing the examples above, you could ask them if they have noticed the 'minus' sign appear on their calculator display.

Resources needed

A blank number line (with about 20 spaces) for each child, pencils, a game sheet (photocopiable sheet 111), a blue and a red dice, and two counters for each pair of children.

What to do

Give each child a blank number line. Tell them to place it lengthwise on the table:

so that the number line goes from left to right, not top to bottom. Tell them to choose any 'step' close to the middle of the line and mark it 0 (zero). Ask them to start on 0 and jump forward six steps. How many steps are they away from 0? Ask them to jump one step back towards 0. Where are they now? Tell them to write that number above that step on the line.

Continue these instructions until they are back at 0. Can they move another step to the left? How far are they away from 0 now? The symbol to denote the negative value, that is –1, can now be introduced. The numbers to the right of 0 could be indicated with a positive sign, for example +3, +4 and so on. Ask the children to complete the number line, and get them to count on from –10 to +10 and back again.

To consolidate the idea of movement along the number line to the left and right of 0, try the following game. Give each pair of children a copy of photocopiable sheet 111, two dice (one blue and one red) and a counter each. Tell them to imagine that they are trapped on the sinking boat shown on the game sheet and that they should use the two dice to reach the safety of the islands. The children should put their counters on 0 and then take it in turns to throw both dice. The number on the red dice indicates the number of steps forward (to the right of 0) they can take. The number on the blue dice indicates the number of steps backwards (to the left of 0) they can take.

For example, if the red dice shows 3 and the blue dice shows 6, they must move three steps to the right, beginning at 0, then six to the left. They will end up at –3. It does not matter in which order the moves are made; six moves to the left and three to the right will result in the same number.

The first player to reach one of the islands is the winner.

Suggestion(s) for extension

Once the children have played this game a few times, they could suggest and play their own variations of the game. Ask them to design a new board game which involves moving forwards and backwards along a line.

Suggestion(s) for support

Play the game with the children. Make the moves carefully, counting out loud as you go; for example, 'The red number is 3, so I move three steps to the right. Now I am on +3. The blue number is 6, so I now move six steps back. I land on –3.' Encourage the children to verbalise each move like this also. The children could colour the island on the right of the sheet in red, and the island on the left in blue. This will help them to remember the direction for each coloured dice.

Assessment opportunities

Observe the children filling in their number lines. Ask them to pick any number on the line and count forwards or backwards. Can they continue counting 'off' the line? Give some simple calculations for them to do using their lines and a counter. For example, 'Start at –4. Now add on 6. Where are you now?' Watch the direction in which the children move along the line. Have they grasped the idea of movement to the left and right of 0?

Observe the children playing the game, noting their moves. Check whether they understand that moving the counter to the left first does not alter the finishing position.

Display ideas

A large number line, marked with negative and positive numbers, can be displayed in the classroom.

Negative numbers game sheet

A set of questions can be written above it: Start at 0. Move forward 6 and backward 7. Where are you now? Use a moveable object on the line so that the children can carry out the problem physically. A cardboard figure with Blu-Tack on the back is a good idea.

Reference to photocopiable sheets
Photocopiable sheet 111 is to be used by each pair of children to play the game described above.

A SHOPPING SPREE

To be able to use decimal notation in money accurately.

†† *Pairs or individuals.*

🕘 *30–45 minutes.*

Previous skills/knowledge needed
The children need to have an understanding of the fact that there are 100 pence in one pound.

Key background information
It is important that children are taught the correct way to write amounts of money. They should know what the pound symbol (£) is and that it is placed before the amount, and that the abbreviation for pence (p) is placed after the amount. It is not correct to use both together. For example, thirty-two pence may be written as 32p or £0.32.

It is vital that children develop the necessary skills of recording amounts of money correctly, both with and without decimal notation. Calculators can be used to record amounts of money over £1 as pence and in decimals of £1. It is important that children do not mix the two ways of recording amounts when they are doing calculations with money. So, for example, if they had to find the total of £6.39 and 73p they should avoid the error of entering 6.39 and 73! Another point to remember when using the calculator to operate with amounts of money is that it will display 7.7 when working out £7.30 plus 40p.

Preparation
There are many opportunities in the primary classroom for giving children experience of solving problems involving money, for example using school dinner money, book club money, weekly pocket money, and so on.

Make sure that the children know the correct way to write amounts of money. If you are making your own worksheets ensure that the prices are realistic and reflect current rates.

Resources needed
A copy of photocopiable sheet 112 for each child, paper, pencils, calculators, money (optional).

What to do
Distribute copies of photocopiable sheet 112 and discuss the prices shown with the children. Make sure that they are able to read the prices and go through the task with them. Read the questions and encourage the children to discuss their work with each other. Ask them to use the calculators to work out the answers to the questions that require arithmetic. When the children have completed the sheet, come together again and discuss the outcomes.

Suggestion(s) for extension
Ask the children to find out how a charity such as OXFAM spends £1 and to represent this information clearly. Some children could make their own shopping spree worksheets using catalogues.

Suggestion(s) for support
Make your own worksheets using lower amounts of money, for example using prices of no more than £1.

Assessment opportunities
Observe the children as they enter the prices in to the calculator, watching out for any child who does not enter the prices in the same format. If the children are tending always to convert pounds and pence to just pence challenge them to see if they can do the reverse.

Opportunities for IT
The children could use a word processor or graphics software to create their own window display. They could experiment with different fonts and print sizes to make the displays eye-catching. They could also write short advertising captions to go with their displays, such as, 'You'll wonder how you ever managed without a....'

Display ideas
The children could create their own 'shop window' containing real items and prices. Various questions could be provided to stimulate discussion together with calculators to make this an interactive display.

Reference to photocopiable sheets
Photocopiable sheet 111 is a stimulus and response sheet that will be needed by each child.

PIECE BY PIECE

To be able to read fraction notation. To recognise simple fractions as part of a unit. To recognise equivalence of simple fractions.

†† *Pairs.*

🕐 *20–30 minutes.*

Previous skills/knowledge needed

The children will need to have had previous experience of handling fractions such as halves and quarters.

Preparation

Discuss the dice with the children. Explain the fraction notation. Give each child a copy of photocopiable sheet 113. Ask the children to prepare the game by cutting out one set of playing pieces and a game board each. It may be easier for them to play the game if each player's pieces are a different colour. This can be achieved by colouring the fraction pieces before they are cut out.

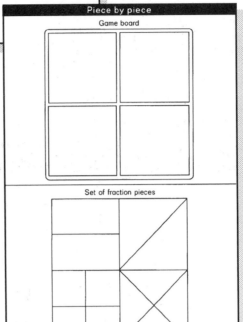

Piece by piece

Game board

Set of fraction pieces

Resources needed

Game board and a set of fraction pieces for each child (photocopiable sheet 113), a dice marked ½, ¼, ¾, ½, ¼, ¾ for each pair.

What to do

Each child needs a game board and a set of fraction pieces. Explain that each square on the game board represents one whole. The aim of the game is to cover all four squares using the fraction pieces. The game is played in pairs. The children take it in turns to throw the dice. If, for example, a child throws ¾ he can put the appropriate piece or pieces on his board:

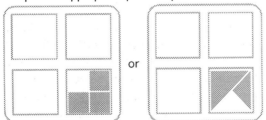

or

Then the other child takes a turn. The winner is the first to cover his board completely.

Suggestion(s) for extension

The set of fraction pieces could be altered to include eighths or sixths, and the markings on the dice changed accordingly, for example ½, ¼, ⅛, ¾, ⅜, ⅝.

Suggestion(s) for support

The dice could be altered to read ½, ½, ½, ¼, ¼, ¼ or the range of fraction shapes could be restricted to one or two types.

Assessment opportunities

Observe the children choosing their fraction pieces when it is their turn. Watch to see if the notation has been correctly interpreted and the variety of ways the child can see to make ¾ or ½.

Display ideas

The children could draw squares and find different ways of shading, say, ¾ of the square. This work could be displayed under the heading '¾ of a square'.

Reference to photocopiable sheet

Photocopiable sheet 113 provides both the game board and the playing pieces for the game. Each child will need one copy of the sheet.

FRACTION FAMILIES

To be able to identify simple equivalent fractions.

†† *Individuals.*

🕐 *20 minutes.*

Previous skills/knowledge needed

Know fraction 'families' of ½, ¼, ⅓, ⅛ and so on.

Key background information

This activity emphasises the idea that the same fraction can be written in different ways. For example, ¼, ²⁄₈, ³⁄₁₂, ⁴⁄₁₆ and so on, are all equivalent fractions and belong to the same 'family', that is the 'family of ¼'. It is important that children should have plenty of experience with the idea of equivalent fractions. Much of the work involving computation with fractions that they will do later on in their mathematics will depend on their understanding of equivalence.

Preparation

Work with the children on equivalence of fractions. Build up tables showing fraction families, for example the '½ family' will include ²⁄₄, ³⁄₆, ⁴⁄₈,⁵⁄₁₀ and so on. Activities to generate such sets of fractions will help to establish the idea of equivalence. Copy photocopiable sheet 114 for each child.

The ½ family

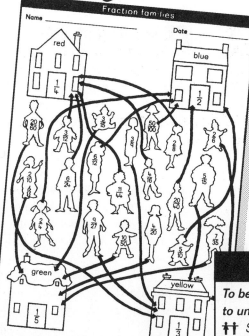

$\frac{1}{2}$				
$\frac{1}{4}$		$\frac{1}{4}$		
$\frac{1}{6}$		$\frac{1}{6}$		$\frac{1}{6}$
$\frac{1}{8}$	$\frac{1}{8}$		$\frac{1}{8}$	$\frac{1}{8}$
$\frac{1}{10}$	$\frac{1}{10}$	$\frac{1}{10}$	$\frac{1}{10}$	$\frac{1}{10}$

and pictures from magazines and catalogues that can be divided into halves or quarters. These could be displayed to show the equivalence of a half and two quarters.

Reference to photocopiable sheet

Photocopiable sheet 114 is a worksheet designed for the children to complete individually. It can be adapted to include additional fractions or a more restricted range for those children who require support. The families are shown on the sheet opposite.

Resources needed

Coloured pencils, a copy of photocopiable sheet 114 for each child.

What to do

Distribute copies of worksheet 114. Tell the children they have to reunite the members of the different families by matching them to the correct house and then colouring them in the appropriate colour. All the members of the ½ family are to be coloured blue, the ¼ family are to be coloured red, the ⅕ family are to be coloured green and the ⅓ family are to be coloured yellow. There are five members of each family.

Once the worksheet has been completed, discuss with the children the fractions they have reunited. What do they notice? Draw their attention to the relationship between the denominators and numerators of each set of fractions (without, necessarily, using those terms). Point out that the fractions in each family are equivalent. Discuss the idea that in any one family there are an unlimited number of equivalent fractions, and that any fraction can only be a 'member' of one family.

Suggestion(s) for extension

The children could make their own version of the worksheet for their friends to do. The members of each family could include decimal fractions and percentages; for example, the '½ family' may include 50%, 0.5, $\frac{3}{6}$ and $\frac{50}{100}$.

Suggestion(s) for support

The children could be given a restricted set of fractions to work with, for example, only ¼ and $\frac{1}{10}$. They may find it useful to use Multilink rods or a fraction diagram such as the one shown above to help them to identify the equivalent fractions.

Assessment opportunities

Review what the children have done on the worksheet and assess their level of understanding through further questioning.

Display ideas

The children could be asked to collect and cut out shapes

MATCHING FRACTIONS

To be able to order simple mixed numbers. To be able to understand the notation of mixed numbers.

†† *Small groups or pairs, then whole class.*

🕐 *30–40 minutes.*

Previous skills/knowledge needed

Ensure that the children have had considerable experience of cutting, colouring and folding shapes and objects into halves and discussing the results.

Preparation

You will need photocopies of sheets 115 and 116 for each pair of children. Cut out the picture cards on photocopiable sheet 115 and the corresponding number cards on photocopiable sheet 116.

Resources needed

For each pair you will need: a set of number cards and a set of picture cards, paper, pencils.

What to do

Give each pair a set of number cards and a set of picture cards. Ask the children to sequence their picture cards in order of size and then to match the number cards to the picture cards.

Once the children have finished this discuss the results as a class. Which is the biggest number? Which is the smallest? Which is bigger ½ or 1? Encourage the children to reach the conclusion that $8\frac{1}{2}$ is bigger than 8 is bigger than $7\frac{1}{2}$ and so on. Then, reminding them of the notation < and > (make some < and > cards as shown below), help them to discuss and record on paper the following:

$8\frac{1}{2} > 8 > 7\frac{1}{2} > 7 > 6\frac{1}{2} > 6 > 5\frac{1}{2} > 5$
$> 4\frac{1}{2} > 4 > 3\frac{1}{2} > 3 > 2\frac{1}{2} > 2 > 1\frac{1}{2} >$
$1 > \frac{1}{2} > 0.$

Encourage the children to think of another way of providing the same information: $0 < \frac{1}{2} < 1 < 1\frac{1}{2}$ and so on.

<
is less than

>
is greater than

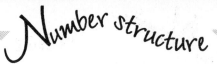

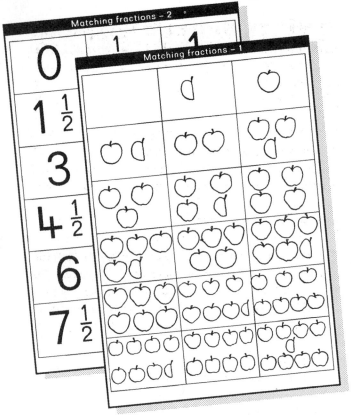

Suggestion(s) for extension

Ask the children to make up another set of cards using $\frac{1}{4}$s or $\frac{1}{3}$s and repeat the activity described above.

Suggestion(s) for support

Some children may find it helpful to play a game of 'Snap' with a partner. One child should take the picture cards while the other uses the number cards. In turns, the children should put down one of their cards face up. If the card put down is equivalent to the previous one, then the first child to shout 'snap' can claim the whole pile and add it to his hand. The winner is the child who claims all the cards first.

Assessment opportunities

Observe the children as they work with the cards. Choose a notation card and ask them to find another that shows a smaller or larger amount. Choose an apple picture card and ask them to find the correct notation card.

Display ideas

Help the children to make a number line from 0 to $8\frac{1}{2}$. Then they can display this alongside two posters showing:

$8\frac{1}{2} > 8 > 7\frac{1}{2} > 7...1 > \frac{1}{2} > 0$ and
$0 < \frac{1}{2} < 1...< 7\frac{1}{2} < 8 < 8\frac{1}{2}$.

Reference to photocopiable sheets

Photocopiable sheets 115 and 116 are reusable resource sheets showing whole numbers and halves from 0 to $8\frac{1}{2}$ pictorially and in mixed number notation respectively. One copy of each is required for each pair of children working at any one time.

WHAT NUMBER AM I?

To be able to use and apply knowledge of fractions to find an answer. To use mathematical reasoning and knowledge to find an answer.

†† *Large group, then pairs.*

🕐 *30–40 minutes.*

Previous skills/knowledge needed

The children should know fractional terms such as $\frac{1}{2}$, $\frac{1}{4}$ and $\frac{1}{5}$, and they should understand the concept of a fraction as part of a whole. Also, they should know some properties of numbers.

Preparation

Make a copy of photocopiable page 117 for each pair.

Resources needed

For each pair you will need: a copy of photocopiable page 117, pencils and writing materials, A4 card, a calculator.

What to do

Explain to the children as a group that you are going to give them a set of clues from which they have to discover a 'missing' number. Explain that the clues demand that they calculate fractional parts of the missing number. Then do the following example on the board. Write the following numbers: 22, 11, 15, 12, 16, 8. Explain that the number they are trying to find is one of these.

Give the following clues in sequence and help the children to guess the number by elimination.

▲ I am larger than $\frac{1}{2}$ of 20;
▲ I am less than $\frac{1}{2}$ of 40;
▲ I am not $\frac{1}{4}$ of 48 or $\frac{1}{2}$ of 32;
▲ $\frac{1}{3}$ of me is 5.

Go through each clue and discuss the possibilities. For example, the first clue, 'I am larger than $\frac{1}{2}$ of 20' will involve them in calculating half of 20. Since the answer is 10, the children can consider which numbers can be eliminated. In this case, 8 can be crossed from the list.

Continue on in this way until only one number remains. (The missing number is 15.)

Distribute photocopiable sheet to each pair of children. Read it through with the children to ensure that everyone understands what to do, and, if necessary, do the first task as a whole group following the procedure described above.

Allow the pairs of children time to work through all the tasks. When they have finished discuss the results. Draw their attention to the different types of clues: for example, refer to those that involved 'less than' and 'more than', or used specific properties of the missing numbers or involved two calculations such as 'I am not $\frac{1}{4}$ of 48 or $\frac{1}{2}$ of 32'.

Challenge the children to make up their own fraction clues

to identify a number. They will need to plan this carefully as a number must be chosen and a set of clues organised which make finding the number possible, but not immediately obvious. Encourage the children to use a variety of clue types. You will need to check their work carefully, ensuring that it is possible to find only one number from the set of clues. Once this has been done the clues can be written out neatly on to A4 card and laminated, if possible. A collection of 'Fraction clue puzzle cards' can be made from these A4 cards for the rest of the children in the class to work on.

Suggestion(s) for extension

Challenge the children to make up missing number puzzles using a mix of vulgar and decimal fractions.

Suggestion(s) for support

Work through a few more examples with the children. Encourage them to work systematically through the sets of clues, crossing out the numbers they know are incorrect.

When making up their own puzzles, start the children off by providing them with a missing number to work on. Choose a number such as 3 or 4. Help them to devise simple clues such as 'I am less than $\frac{1}{2}$ of 10'.

Assessment opportunities

Note the strategies children use in tackling this task. Do they adopt a systematic approach in eliminating the options?

Collect and check the assessment evidence the children produce: the completed worksheets and the puzzles they create themselves.

Opportunities for IT

The children could use a word processor and simple graphics package to present and publish their own 'What number am I?' problem. These could then be collated as a class display or in a class book for the children to use.

Reference to photocopiable sheet

Photocopiable sheet 117 provides a set of fraction number puzzles. The answers to these puzzles are shown on the sheet above: 6, 75, 36, 10, 48, 250.

FRACTION OF 100

To begin to relate equivalence of fractions and percentages.

†† *Individuals.*

🕐 *30–40 minutes.*

Previous skills/knowledge needed

The children should be familiar with fractions such as halves, quarters, thirds and so on, and with generating fraction families.

Key background information

A percentage is a proportion or ratio whose denominator is 100. The term *per cent* (Latin) means 'in every 100' (*per* meaning 'for each', *centum* meaning 'a hundred'). For example, 5% is $\frac{5}{100}$; five parts out of 100. It is important that the children understand the meaning of a percentage before they become involved in calculations using them.

Preparation

Copy photocopiable sheet 118 for each child.

Resources needed

Centimetre squared paper cut into 10×10cm squares, coloured pencils, a copy of photocopiable sheet 118 for each child.

What to do

Give the children a 10×10cm square each. Ask them to fold it into two equal parts and shade one half. Using a different colour ask them to shade a quarter of the square. How many small squares have they coloured as half of the large square? How many small squares are there in the quarter section? How many small squares have they shaded altogether?

The children should be able to see the relationship that: $\frac{50}{100}$ is the same as $\frac{1}{2}$; $\frac{25}{100}$ is the same as $\frac{1}{4}$; and $\frac{75}{100}$ is the same as $\frac{3}{4}$. The term 'percentage' could be introduced at this point and the children shown that 1% is equivalent to $\frac{1}{100}$ and 50% is equivalent to $\frac{50}{100}$ and so on.

Provide each child with a copy of photocopiable sheet 118. The children should then work through the sheet, shading the fractions of the squares and recording them as percentages. The denominators involved are all factors of 100, so converting the fractions into hundredths is relatively easy.

Suggestion(s) for extension

Some children can be shown how to find out how many hundredths are equivalent to, say, $\frac{8}{32}$. This can be done using the calculator:

$$\frac{8}{32} = 8 \div 32$$
$$= 0.25$$
$$= 25\%$$

Suggestion(s) for support

Revise the 'Fraction of 100' photocopiable sheet so each question refers to hundredths; for example, ask the children to shade $\frac{20}{100}$, $\frac{60}{100}$, $\frac{50}{100}$ and so on.

Assessment opportunities

Ask the children to create some fractions and percentages of their own. Observe their strategies and discuss the process with them to assess their level of understanding.

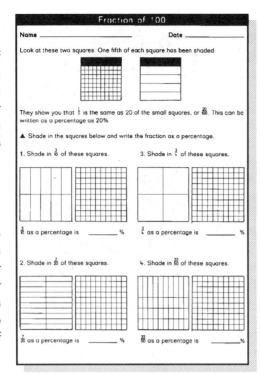

Display ideas

Ask the children to transfer some of their work on to larger 100 squares and label them clearly with the fraction/percentage shaded. These can be cut out, mounted and displayed as part of an overall display on percentages.

Reference to photocopiable sheets

Photocopiable sheet 118 is a worksheet that the children may complete individually, or in pairs.

PERCENTAGE PATTERNS

To understand that a percentage means 'out of 100'.
To be able to recognise the equivalence of fractions (in hundredths) and percentages.

†† *Individuals.*

🕐 *30–45 minutes.*

Previous skills/knowledge needed

The children should have had practical experience of fractions and have a basic understanding of percentages.

What to do

Give each child a copy of photocopiable worksheet 119. Explain that they are each to draw five different simple patterns in the boxes at the top of the sheet. Any type of pattern can be drawn: spots, stripes or different colours. They should then use those patterns to fill in the squares on the 100 square. It does not matter which of the squares are used for each pattern. When that is finished they are to

complete the table at the bottom of the page. This asks them to record the total number of squares they have used each pattern for in terms of a fraction and a percentage.

Suggestion(s) for extension

Ask the children to throw a dice 100 times, to tally up the outcomes and to record them as percentages.

Suggestion(s) for support

Discuss the completion of the table with the children. Talk about the equivalence of 'percentage' and 'out of a hundred', but avoid using mathematical notation – use everyday language instead.

Assessment opportunities

Through discussion check the children's understanding of the equivalence of 'percentage' and 'out of a hundred'.

Display ideas

The children could transfer the patterns they devised during the activity on to larger 100 squares using felt-tipped pens. Display these along with the relevant information concerning the percentages used.

Ask the children to collect photographs of tiled areas and to describe their patterns using percentages; for example, so many red tiles in 20 is so many %.

Reference to photocopiable sheet

Photocopiable worksheet 119 is an individual recording sheet. One copy will be needed for each child taking part in the activity.

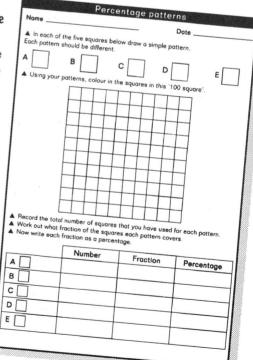

Number relationships

Developing an understanding of number includes recognising the relationships between numbers and using these relationships to develop effective strategies for computation. The ability to see patterns in numbers, understand sequences and anticipate how a pattern will continue all contribute to competence in understanding and carrying out operations with numbers.

The programme of study for number contains references which reflect the need for children to understand the relationships between numbers. The three sections in this chapter contain activities which aim to promote this understanding. Aspects of number relationships are addressed in turn under the headings of: Patterns, Number facts and Special numbers.

Mathematics has been described as the search for pattern and order. Most children enjoy looking for patterns and trying to make sense of their experiences with numbers. A child observing a pattern and explaining why it is formed is engaged in mathematics at his or her own level. The first section of this chapter (pages 28–34) is designed to encourage children to explore number patterns and sequences and to reflect upon their own strategies by exploring 100 squares, magic squares, Pascal's triangle and so on. Recognising, remembering and using mathematical patterns can simplify many tasks and can help with the acquisition of number facts.

The second section of the chapter (pages 34–45) contains activities which give children practice in the use of these facts including number bonds and multiplication facts.

Finally, the third part of the chapter (pages 45–54) covers 'special' numbers such as factors, multiples, primes, spatial numbers and index notation.

THE 100 SQUARE

To recognise and explain number patterns, including patterns made by multiples, on a 100 square. To recognise relationships between sets of multiples.

†† *Large groups.*

🕐 *30–45 minutes.*

Previous skills/knowledge needed

The children will need to have knowledge of cardinal numbers (indicating quantity: 1, 2, 3...). They should understand the process of multiplication and have had some experience exploring patterns of multiples.

Key background information

The 100 square can be used to explore a whole variety of number patterns and relationships. It is a good idea to have a ready supply of them in your classroom within easy access for the children to use as they would other pieces of mathematics apparatus.

Preparation

Complete the blank 100 square (on photocopiable sheet 120) with the numbers from 1 to 100. Use this as a master copy and make at least four copies for each child.

Discuss with the children the meaning of the term 'multiple' (a number that may be divided by another a certain number of times without a remainder: 56 is a multiple of 7, for example).

Resources needed

At least four 100 squares for each child, coloured pencils.

What to do

Give each child several of the 100 squares. Tell them to look at one of the squares and look for patterns among the numbers. Ask them to describe their patterns to the rest of the group. The set of multiples of 10 and 5 may be identified.

Now tell the children to colour every second square (using the same colour) to reveal a pattern of alternate columns covering all the multiples of 2. Point out to the children that these are the even numbers and draw attention to the pattern they make on the 100 square. Ask them what pattern they think they would get if they coloured all the odd numbers? They may notice that these are the numbers that have not been coloured.

Ask the children to use a different colour and circle all the multiples of 4. Then ask them to choose another colour to put a cross on all the multiples of 8. This will demonstrate the relationship between these three sets of multiples. Discuss this with the children.

On the second 100 square they can do the same for the multiples of 3, 6 and 9. Ask them to explain the patterns they can see.

Using another 100 square, the children should colour all the multiples of 3 in yellow and the multiples of 4 in blue. Ask them which numbers are coloured green now (those coloured both yellow and blue)? Tell them to look at the yellow numbers. Can they describe them? What about the blue numbers? What can they say about the numbers that have not been coloured? As before, encourage the children to explain what they have done.

Ask the children to do the same for the multiples of 3 and 5 on another 100 square, but colouring the multiples of 3 in red and the multiples of 5 in yellow. This time ask them which numbers will be coloured orange and so on.

The activity can continue with the children exploring other combinations of sets of multiples using additional copies of the 100 square. Get the children to describe and explain their results for each combination they try.

Suggestion(s) for extension

Discuss with the children the numbers which do not appear in any of the sets of multiples. The activity 'Sieving out primes' (page 50) may be a suitable extension activity also.

The completed 1–100 100 square can be used also to explore the patterns made by colouring in the square numbers and triangular numbers.

Suggestion(s) for support

First get the children to colour each set of multiples on a separate numbered 100 square. When they have completed all ten sets of multiples ask them questions such as: Which multiples give diagonal lines? Can you explain why? Look at the patterns made by the multiples of 2, 5 and 10. What have they got in common?

Encourage the children to find numbers that are coloured in two of the sets of multiples, or three of the sets of multiples. Are there any numbers that are coloured in four of the sets?

The children could also try identifying multiples by piling up cubes of different colours on an enlarged 100 square. Tell them to put, say, a red cube on each multiple of 2, then a blue cube on each multiple of 3 and so on for ten different colours/multiples. Those numbers with the highest towers of cubes are multiples of the most numbers/have the most factors.

Assessment opportunities

To use the tasks described above for assessing a particular child, make sure that you ask lots of questions in order to give them a chance to describe and explain the relationships between sets of multiples. Note individual children's speed and confidence when identifying the multiples of different numbers. Have they a good knowledge of the multiplication facts to 10 × 10?

Opportunities for IT

There is software available which will automatically colour in specified multiples on a 100 square. This helps the children to see quickly the patterns as they emerge. The same task could also be undertaken using framework software like *My World* (Derbyshire LEA/SEMERC) where the children can drag different coloured markers over any square. The results could be printed out for display.

Alternatively, a simple graphics programme could be used with a 100 square which you have drawn in, with the children using different coloured blocks of markers to shade or identify the different multiples. If you create a number of different coloured markers and position them around the edge of the

number square the children could be introduced to simple copy commands so that they can make more copies of the markers before dragging them to the appropriate squares.

Display ideas

The patterns produced by colouring the multiples on the 100 squares by hand or on the computer can be put together to make an attractive display. If the list of multiples is written out clearly on each square this can act as a visual support for the learning and memorising of multiplication facts.

Reference to photocopiable sheets

Photocopiable sheet 120 is used for this activity. Extend and complete the sheet with the numbers from 1 to 100. The children will need at least four of these 100 squares. 100 squares can be used for a variety of maths activities including identifying number patterns.

SEEING SQUARES

To be able to recognise a number pattern and use square numbers.

†† *Large group, then individuals.*

🕐 *30–45 minutes.*

Previous skills/knowledge needed

The children should have been introduced to simple number patterns. They should be familiar with the process of multiplication.

Key background information

This exploratory activity involves the children in a search for patterns, to be discovered by finding the number of squares in different-sized square grids.

Preparation

Make a copy of photocopiable worksheet 121 for each child.

Resources needed

Board or flipchart and marker pen, centimetre squared paper, coloured pencils, a copy of photocopiable worksheet 121 for each child.

What to do

Begin by drawing on the board or flipchart a large square divided into four smaller squares (as shown on the next page).

Make sure all the children can see what you are doing. Ask them how many squares they can see altogether. If some of the children answer 'four', ask them to look again. There are four small squares and one large square. So there are five squares all together.

Tell the children that they are going to do an activity that will involve them in finding squares within squares. Distribute copies of photocopiable worksheet 121. Each child will need a supply of centimetre squared paper and coloured pencils too.

Now draw a 4 × 4 grid on the board (as shown opposite). Explain to the children how you have shaded part of the 4 × 4 grid to make a 2 × 2 square. Ask them if they can see any other squares the same size as the shaded one. They can use the centimetre squared paper to investigate how many there are. You may want to suggest they draw a separate 4 × 4 grid for each 2 × 2 square they find. Give them time to discover that there are nine 2 × 2 squares. Then draw their attention to the table on photocopiable sheet 121. Tell them they are going to look for other–sized squares and that they are to put their results in the table printed on the sheet. Show them how to fill in the table. They have found that there are nine 2 × 2 squares within the 4 × 4 grid, so tell them to find 4 × 4 down the left-hand side of the table and move along to the second column labelled '2cm squares' and put a 9 in that box.

Encourage the children to complete the table. Make sure that they understand that for each grid you want them to find different-sized squares.

Encourage the children to draw their own grids carefully, making sure that they can prove to you how many smaller squares they have found. They should see a pattern emerge as they complete the table. Discuss with them the fact that all the numbers in the table are square numbers. Can they see why?

Can they tell you how many 2cm squares there would be in a 7 × 7 grid? Can they complete another line of the table without using squared paper to draw the grids?

To end the activity, discuss with the children the ways they have drawn the grids and kept a record of how many squares they have found within them.

Suggestion(s) for extension

The children can continue their table of results up to a 10 × 10 grid. Encourage them to predict the number of different-sized squares they will find. Can they now work out the number of different-sized squares that can be identified on a chessboard?

Suggestion(s) for support

Make sure the children are systematic in the way they search for the squares. Spend some time with each child, discussing the pattern of numbers emerging. Ask them if they have seen this pattern of numbers before. Ensure they know the square numbers.

Assessment opportunities

Use the completed tables to check whether the children have discovered the correct number of squares. How the children have continued the table will tell you if they recognised the pattern as being the square numbers. The extension activity will show evidence of the children's ability to generalise their results.

Display ideas

Examples of the children's work could be mounted and displayed.

Set out a chessboard with the question, 'How many squares can you see?' next to it. The solution, along with how the children tackled the problem, can be displayed alongside.

Reference to photocopiable sheet

Photocopiable worksheet 121 provides a chart on which the children can record their results for this investigation. You will need one copy of this sheet for each child. The completed chart should look like the one shown opposite.

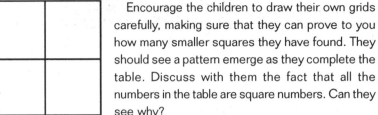

Grid size	1cm square	2cm squares	3cm squares	4cm squares	5cm squares	6cm squares
1 × 1	1					
2 × 2	4	1				
3 × 3	9	4	1			
4 × 4	16	9	4	1		
5 × 5	25	16	9	4	1	
6 × 6	36	25	16	9	4	1

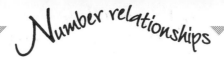
SQUARE MAGIC

To look at patterns in magic squares.

†† *Individuals or small groups.*

⏱ *30–45 minutes.*

Previous skills/knowledge needed

The children should have prior knowledge of the cardinal numbers (1, 2, 3...) and must be able to add together two-digit numbers.

Make sure that they understand the terms 'row', 'column', and 'diagonal'.

Key background information

Magic squares have been around for a long time. Supposedly, the very first magic square was drawn on the back of a tortoise seen by a Chinese emperor around 2000 BC. A magic square is a matrix of numbers arranged in rows and columns so that the sum of each row, column and diagonal is the same – that is 'magic'.

All magic squares have a basic pattern which is formed from the numbers 1, 2, 3, ... 9. The total given by each line of the basic 3 × 3 square is 15, which is known as the 'magic constant' for this square.

Once a magic square has been made, more can be derived from it by adding, subtracting, dividing or multiplying each number in the square by the same number.

Preparation

Make copies of worksheet 122 for each child. The grids on the bottom half of the page are for any children doing the extension work for this activity. Delete them if you feel they are inappropriate.

Resources needed

Centimetre squared paper, pencils, a copy of photocopiable worksheet 122 for each child, calculators (optional).

What to do

Draw an example of a 3 × 3 magic square on the board (as shown here). Tell the children that the square you have drawn is magic. Do they know *why* it is magic? Ask them to add the numbers in each row of the grid and then to add the numbers in each column and then those in the two diagonals. What do they notice? They will tell you that the

8	3	4
1	5	9
6	7	2

rows, columns and diagonals each add up to 15. Explain to them that 15 is the magic number of the square.

Distribute photocopiable worksheet 122. Explain that they have to complete the magic squares at the top of the sheet so that all the rows, columns and diagonals total 15. Encourage them to draw some 3 × 3 grids on to centimetre squared paper to try out their ideas before they put their final answers on the sheet.

Suggestion(s) for extension

Ask the children to choose one of their completed squares. What do they think would happen if they added the same number, say 10, to each number in the square? Get them to do this to make a new square. Ask questions such as: Is your new square magic? What is its magic number? What if you multiplied all the numbers in your new square by 3? Will it still be magic?

Get the children to make more new magic squares. Encourage them to try using division and subtraction too. They could use calculators to speed up the process. Tell them to record their work using the blank magic squares at the bottom of sheet 122.

Suggestion(s) for support

Show the children some more examples of magic squares. Ask them to use a calculator to determine whether they are magic or not and to find the magic number for each one.

Before giving the children worksheet 122, fill in some more of the numbers to make the task slightly easier.

Assessment opportunities

Ask the children to show you their completed sheets and discuss the work with them. Establish whether they have combined the numbers together correctly to reach 15.

Opportunities for IT

The children could explore magic squares using a simple spreadsheet, either set up in advance by the teacher or set up by the children themselves.

By typing in the numbers into the magic square spreadsheet cells the results are automatically calculated and the answers placed in the appropriate cells. This would enable the children to model their magic square and see the effect of changing any one number in the square in one go.

The square could be set up as follows:

A	B	C	D	E
1				D2+C3+B4
2				SUM(B2;D2)
3				SUM(B3;D3)
4				SUM(B4;D4)
5	SUM(B2;B4)	SUM(C2;C4)	SUM(D2;D4)	B2+C3+D4
6				

Once the children have played with the basic 3 × 3 square, they could experiment in setting up the formulae for a 4 × 4 square, or changing the rules for the square.

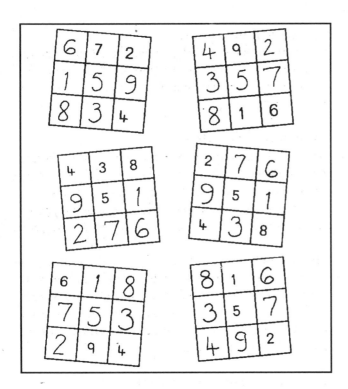

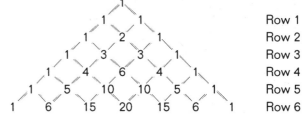

numbers within its rows and diagonals. The triangle itself was known as early as AD 1300, when it was published in China. Hence, it is often referred to as the 'Chinese triangle'. It was the French mathematician, Blaise Pascal (1623–62) who first brought it to the attention of mathematicians in the Western world. It was his extensive work on the triangle which caused it to be named after him.

The triangle is an arrangement of numbers; each number in each row of the triangle is formed by adding the pair of numbers directly above it, to the left and right. Starting with 1 at the top (which is considered to be row 0), the first six rows of the triangle are:

1	1		Row 1
1	2	1	Row 2
1	3	3	1	Row 3
1 4 6 4 1			Row 4
1 5 10 10 5 1			Row 5
1 6 15 20 15 6 1			Row 6

Display ideas

Find as many different examples of magic squares as you can. Enlarge a few of them, omitting some of the numbers. They can be displayed for the children to complete as part of a puzzle corner. Research, or let the children research, the history of the magic square in the school library and mount everyone's findings alongside the puzzles.

Reference to photocopiable sheets

Photocopiable worksheet 122 provides six magic squares for the children to complete (some answers are given above) and some blank grids to be used by the children to create new magic squares as part of the extension work.

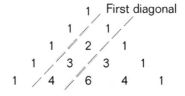

PASCAL'S TRIANGLE

To introduce the pattern of numbers known as 'Pascal's triangle'. To explore number patterns within the triangle.

†† *Large groups, then individuals.*

🕐 *45 minutes.*

Previous skills/knowledge needed

The children should be able to add two- and three-digit numbers. They should be familiar with number patterns and should be able to identify a diagonal pattern of numbers.

Key background information

The pattern of numbers know as 'Pascal's triangle' provides many opportunities for children to explore the sequences of

Preparation

When copying photocopiable pages 123 and 124 for each child, it would be a good idea to copy and complete the sheets for yourself. As well as being useful for reference purposes, this will help you to discover some of the patterns contained within the triangle for yourself.

Resources needed

Several copies of photocopiable sheet 123 and a copy of the puzzle on-sheet 124 for each child, paper, pencils, calculators.

What to do

Give the children a copy of photocopiable sheet 123 each and ask them to look carefully at the numbers at the top of the triangle.

Discuss with them how each number is produced. Draw their attention to the line of 1s down either side of the triangle. Ask them if they have noticed any other patterns. They may recognise the counting numbers on the first diagonal. Place a ruler along the diagonal to make the numbers clearer:

```
              1  First diagonal
           1     1
        1     2     1
     1     3     3     1
  1     4     6     4     1
```

They should also notice the symmetry of the numbers along the rows.

When the children have discovered that each number in the triangle is found by adding the two numbers above it,

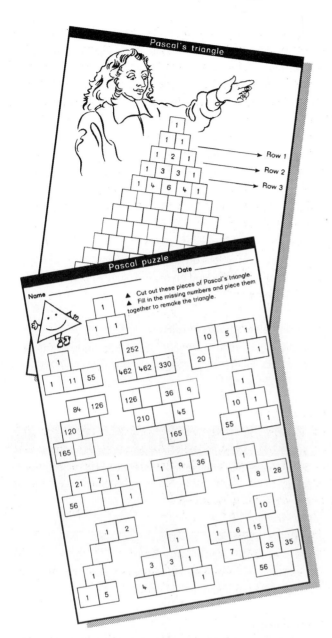

ask them if they can complete the triangle on the photocopiable page. The numbers get quite large, and calculators will be useful for this activity.

Stop the children after a short while and ask them whether they have to work out *every* number on the triangle by adding two numbers? By this time, they should have noticed that the triangular numbers occur on the second diagonal.

Allow the children time to complete the triangle. Encourage them to search for further patterns – there are many to discover.

Suggestion(s) for extension

The children could look at the even and odd numbers on the triangle. Ask them to shade in all the odd numbers. They will discover patterns of equilateral triangles.

Colouring in the multiples of different numbers will produce interesting patterns also. Let the children use a new copy of the completed triangle for each new pattern investigation.

Suggestion(s) for support

It is important that the children grasp the addition rule for producing new numbers on the triangle. Discuss this rule with them, and then go through the first few rows of the triangle together.

Assessment opportunities

Listen to the children and ascertain how many different patterns they can see in the triangle.

Give them the puzzle on photocopiable worksheet 124. Their competence in completing the puzzle should tell you if they have understood the addition rule behind the triangle.

Display ideas

Enlarge a copy of a completed triangle and mount it on brightly-coloured card. Display this along with the children's work on the patterns contained within the triangle. The shaded patterns produced from the extension activities will make an attractive addition to the display.

Reference to photocopiable sheets

Photocopiable sheet 123 provides a triangular grid with the first five rows of Pascal's triangle filled in.

Photocopiable sheet 124 presents a puzzle which can be used for assessment purposes.

NUMBER STATEMENTS

To use knowledge of properties of numbers to find relationships between two numbers.

†† *Group of four to six children.*
🕐 *30–45 minutes.*

Previous skills/knowledge needed

The children should know about some of the properties of cardinal numbers: odds/evens, multiples and so on.

Preparation

Make a set of 1–50 number cards for each group. Cards for 0–9 are given on photocopiable sheet 106. Further copies of this page could be amended for the numbers 10–19, 20–29 and so on. Cut the sheets into individual cards and laminate them to prolong their life as a handy classroom resource.

Resources needed

Paper, pencils, calculators, one pack of 1–50 cards per group.

What to do

This activity can be used at different levels, depending upon what children know about number. At any level it will involve them in a lot of discussion with both you, their teacher, and each other.

Sit down with the group of children. Show them two

number cards: 6 and 19, for example. Ask the children what they can tell you about these two numbers. Together, write down some statements about them. Give them one to start them off: 6 is less than 19.

Encourage the children to share their ideas and make a list of their suggestions. They will often have ideas you have not thought of; some examples may be:

▲ 3 lots of 6 plus 1 makes 19;

▲ The sum of 6 and 19 is 25, which is a square number;

▲ 19 minus 6 is a prime number.

When you feel they have found enough 'statements', tell them they are going to play a 'number statement' game. Explain the rules to them as follows. The number cards are shuffled and placed face down on the table. The top two cards are turned over. Each player in turn has to make a statement about these two numbers. The other players in the group have to discuss this statement and decide if it is valid or not. The statement can only count if the group agree that it is correct. The next player must make a different statement and the same process of validation is carried out. Play continues until all the possibilities they know have been exhausted. Each player must keep a written record of his statements. The person with the most valid statements is the winner of that round. The cards can then be returned to the bottom of the pack and the next two top cards turned over for the next round.

The children may want to use a calculator to check each other's statements. Ensure that they give each other enough time to take their turn and encourage them to write down all their ideas while they are waiting their turn.

Suggestion(s) for extension

Encourage the children to use their calculators to explore the two numbers revealed during the game and to use their knowledge of special numbers such as primes, factors, triangular numbers and so on.

If a few rounds of this game are played, the children could compile a book entitled *Number properties*. This would be a reference book explaining and listing different kinds of numbers. Compiling such a book could be a group activity over a period of days.

Suggestion(s) for support

The game can be played in pairs and the numbers used restricted to 1–9. Some children may need to use materials such as number lines, calculators or base 10 equipment to check the statements.

Assessment opportunities

By observing the children as a group playing the game or watching how an individual child tackles the activity, you will be able to assess how they use their existing knowledge of numbers to find new relationships.

Display ideas

Write out two numbers on large cards. Display the children's lists of statements around them. The *Number properties* book could form part of the display.

Reference to photocopiable sheet

You may wish to use one or more ammended copies of photocopiable sheet 106 to prepare the 1–50 number cards used for this activity.

ADD AND SUBTRACT RACE

To be able to use knowledge of addition and subtraction facts.

†† *Pairs.*

🕐 *30 minutes.*

Previous skills/knowledge needed

The children should understand the process of addition and subtraction using numbers up to 20.

Preparation

Make a copy of photocopiable sheet 125 for each pair of children. If possible, mount the copies on to card and laminate them.

Resources needed

A copy of photocopiable sheet 125, a calculator and two counters in different colours for each pair.

What to do

Give each pair of children a copy of photocopiable sheet 125, a calculator and two counters.

In their pairs, tell each player to place a counter on the 0 at the start of one of the tracks. The players must choose who will go first and then take turns. The first player has to decide what to do and mentally perform the necessary sum – an addition to move from 0 to 8. She says 'Add 8'. This is checked using the calculator. If she is correct, she can move her counter to that square. (When it is her turn again she will begin with 8 and have to reach 13.) If she is incorrect she can do nothing and play passes to the other player. It is then the turn of the second player. Play continues with both children having to add or subtract mentally in order to move their counters. The first player to reach the finishing number of 20 is the winner.

At various points the track splits into two. The players may decide which route to take. Encourage them to look ahead at the numbers – the easiest route is not always the quickest!

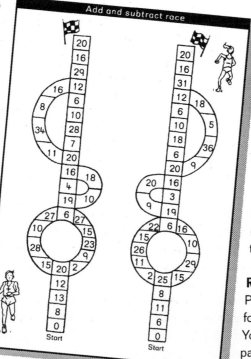
Add and subtract race

Suggestion(s) for extension
Make a version of the game using numbers from 0 to 50 or a version where a number larger than 10 must be added or subtracted each time. Let the children make their own games with numbers and track shapes of their own choice.

Suggestion(s) for support
Let the children have two guesses at each number they need to add or subtract to reach the next square.

Make a version of the game using only numbers 0–15.

Assessment opportunities
Observe individual children playing the game. Do they find the calculation correctly most of the time? Discuss with them

how they work out the number needed to reach the next square. Determine whether they are able to recall quickly addition and subtraction facts to 20.

Display ideas
Ask the children to make a large number track similar to the game board and mount it round the classroom. The track could have a theme, such as a trek through the jungle, and be decorated appropriately. Use the track on a regular basis, by asking the children to take a turn each to move from one end of the track to the other.

Reference to photocopiable sheets
Photocopiable page 125 provides the tracks for playing the 'Add and subtract race' game. You will need a copy of this page for each pair of children.

ADDITION SQUARES

To be able to recall knowledge of addition facts to complete addition grids.

†† *Individuals, then pairs.*

🕐 *45 minutes.*

Previous skills/knowledge needed
The children should understand the operation of addition and have had lots of experience adding numbers to 20. Being able to provide quick responses to addition problems involving numbers less than 20 is an important skill and will help them with work involving larger numbers.

Key background information
The following activity will give the children practice in solving simple addition sums by asking them to compile an addition square and then solve smaller, incomplete addition squares.

This activity will provide opportunities to develop understanding of the commutative property of addition – that is, that 3 + 4 is the same as 4 + 3.

Preparation
Make two copies of photocopiable sheet 120. Extend and complete them as a 1–10 and a blank addition square:

+	1	2	3	4	5	6
1						
2						
3						
4						
5						

+						

Use these pages as master copies and make further copies for each child. Each child will also need a copy of photocopiable sheet 126.

Resources needed
Centimetre squared paper, pencils, a copy of the 1–10 and the blank addition squares (see 'Preparation' above) and a copy of photocopiable worksheet 126 for each child.

What to do
Give each of the children a copy of the blank 1–10 addition square. Explain that they are going to fill it in by adding the numbers along the top row and in the first column. If necessary, remind them that columns go up and down and rows go across. Demonstrate how to fill in the square. Choose an example, say 6 + 7, and ask them to find the 6 column and then the 7 row. Explain how to put 13 in the square where they cross, because 6 + 7 = 13. You may need to provide a few more examples to ensure that all the children understand how the square is filled in. Then give them time to complete the whole addition square. When they have finished, time can be spent discussing the patterns that they may have noticed on the square.

Draw their attention to the central diagonal line. What pattern can they see? Have they noticed how the numbers on the square are laid out symmetrically about this diagonal?

Now ask the children to construct another addition square using the completely blank grid; this time they should change the order of the numbers along the horizontal and/or vertical line. They should then swap their addition squares with their partners and challenge each other to complete the new square in as quick a time as possible.

Go on to tell the children that we can have much smaller addition squares and draw an example of one for them.

+	5	7
3	8	10
5	10	12

Give out copies of photocopiable worksheet 126 and ask the children to fill in the addition squares on the page. This sheet provides them with ten examples of small addition squares. Some of them show the 'answers', but not the questions. When the children have completed the sheet ask them to compare their results with a partner. Is there only one way of filling in each square?

Suggestion(s) for extension
The children could make an addition square using the completely blank grid and the numbers 11 to 20 in the first row and column. Ask them to invent their own small addition squares for other children to complete. The idea could also be extended to the operation of multiplication.

Suggestion(s) for support
Work closely with the children when they are filling in the original 1–10 addition square. If they are not sure of the addition facts to 10 they will need further activities which will reinforce this knowledge.

Instead of swapping their new addition squares with their partners, they could complete them themselves and time how long it takes them. Make some copies of their new squares. They could attempt to complete the square at regular intervals, each time trying to shorten the length of time it takes them.

Assessment opportunities
By observing how quickly and confidently individual children complete the addition squares, you will gain some idea of how well they can recall addition facts.

Opportunities for IT
The children could build up a range of addition squares using a spreadsheet. They would need to be shown how the coordinate system works and how to write a simple formula which added the values of two squares. The spreadsheet might look something like this:

A	B	C	D	E
1	1	2	3	4
2	2	B2+C1	B2+D1	B2+E1
3	3	B3+C1	B2+D1	B3+E1
4	4	B4+C1	B4+D1	B4+E1
5	5			
6	6			

Children with more experience could be shown how to replicate the formula across or down the cells to speed up the process of creating the square.

Once it has been created, changing the numbers in the B column or the 1 row will immediately recalculate the square.

Display ideas

A large copy of a completed addition square could be displayed in a prominent place in the classroom. Puzzle cards containing smaller, incomplete squares could be put beside it with a notice inviting the children to try the activities.

Reference to photocopiable sheets

Photocopiable sheet 120 provides a blank 100 square, copies of which can be adapted into a 1–10 and a completely blank addition square. Photocopiable sheet 126 gives ten examples of smaller addition squares to be completed. The children will need at least one copy of each of these sheets for this activity.

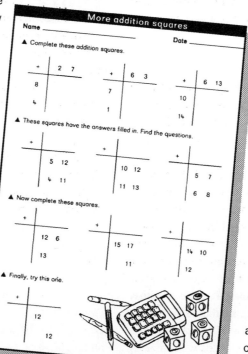

CROSS-NUMBERS

To be able to recall number facts using addition and subtraction.

†† *Individuals.*

🕐 *45 minutes.*

Previous skills/knowledge needed

The children should understand the process of addition and subtraction. They should have experience of adding and subtracting two-digit numbers.

Preparation

You may wish to discuss with the children the idea behind a crossword. Many of them will have come across crosswords either in newspapers and comics or in children's puzzle books. However, they may not know how to fill one in. Collect a few examples of crosswords to show the children.

Copy photocopiable sheet 127 directly on to card for each child. Alternatively, mount the copies on card. If possible, cover them with clear adhesive plastic or laminate them.

Resources needed

A copy of photocopiable worksheet 127 for each child, 1cm or 2cm squared paper, pencils.

What to do

Explain to the children that they are going to do some puzzles

like crosswords, only these puzzles are not about words, they are about numbers. They are called 'cross-numbers'. The clues are given in the form of calculations which the children have to work out.

Distribute photocopiable sheet 127. Make sure the children understand how to use the clues and the grids. They should know that the answers to the clues are placed in the squares, either across or down. Do the first across and down clues with them, demonstrating where to place the answers. Then let the children complete the cross-numbers sheet.

Now, using the squared paper, ask the children to invent their own cross-number puzzles using addition and subtraction for the clues. When they have made a new puzzle, the clues should be written out carefully alongside a blank outline. They should check their cross-numbers carefully. The clues and the blank outline could be photocopied and several copies made so that the puzzles can be presented for other children to complete.

Suggestion(s) for extension

Allow the children to invent a second cross-number using all four operations, or they could make the clues more difficult by using larger numbers.

Suggestion(s) for support

Let the children use a calculator to work out the clues and check their answers. When making their own puzzles, encourage the children to use a small grid and limit the number of clues.

Assessment opportunities

Observe individual children working on the cross-number puzzles. Note how accurately (and quickly) they are able to recall addition and subtraction facts in order to complete the puzzles. The completed sheet can be used as evidence of a child's accuracy with addition and subtraction.

Opportunities for IT

The children might use a simple graphics package to present their cross-numbers. A simple grid can be drawn, the blocked squares filled with colour and the clue numbers positioned in the corner of squares using a smaller font. The activity could be used to extend the children's experience and skills in using a package for presenting their work.

They would need to be shown how to:
▲ draw lines, perhaps using a background grid with 'snap to grid' options set so that it is easy to draw straight lines;
▲ colour in squares;
▲ write text (or numbers) and change the font size, and then move the number to the appropriate square.

The clues could be added using the graphics package or the completed square placed in a word processing package that can handle graphics and the clues typed. Multiple copies can then be printed for children to try; or the class's contributions printed, bound and published as a class project.

Display ideas

Ask groups of children to devise their own display-sized cross-numbers and mount them on a display board. Provide small copies of each of the cross-numbers alongside the board. Ask each group to complete the cross-numbers devised by the other groups in spare moments over a period of time – say, two weeks. Then, as a class, complete the display cross-numbers referring to the groups' solutions.

Reference to photocopiable sheet

Photocopiable sheet 127 offers several cross-number puzzles involving simple addition and subtraction clues. The children will each need a copy of this page. The solutions are:

A.
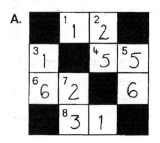

B.
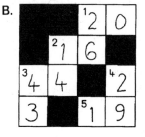

C.
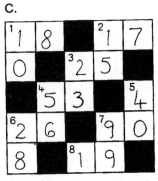

D.
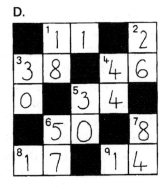

MULTIPLICATION SQUARE

To make a multiplication square and explore the patterns within it. To be able to recall multiplication facts 10 × 10.

†† *Individuals.*

🕐 *30–40 minutes.*

Previous skills/knowledge needed

The children should be familiar with the multiplication tables up to 10 × 10.

Key background information

Constructing a multiplication square by filling in the numbers involves the children in writing out the multiplication facts to 10 × 10. As they complete the table it will help to fix those facts in their memories.

Preparation

Draw a 10 × 10 square on 2cm squared paper. Cut this out and mount it on card. This will be the master copy for the 10 × 10 square the children will use. Copy the square so that you have one for each child.

Resources needed

2cm squared paper, a copy of the blank 10 × 10 square (see 'Preparation') for each child, pencils, scissors, card, board or flipchart or large sheet of paper, marker pen.

What to do

Give each child a piece of 2cm squared paper and a blank 10 × 10 square (20 × 20cm). Tell the children that they are going to build up all the multiplication facts to 10 × 10. Then draw the following rectangle on to the board or on a large piece of paper:

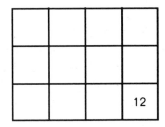

Explain to the children that this rectangle represents the multiplication fact 3 × 4 = 12. There are 3 rows and 4 columns, which give 12 squares altogether. The total number of squares, the product, is written in the bottom right-hand square.

Can any of the children give you another example of a multiplication fact and draw the corresponding rectangle?

Go through three or four examples together. Then tell the children to draw some rectangles for themselves using the squared paper and cut them out.

When they have a collection of rectangles, show the children how these should be placed against the top left-hand corner of the blank 10 × 10 square they have been given and the numbers on them copied into the corresponding squares on the 10 × 10 square:

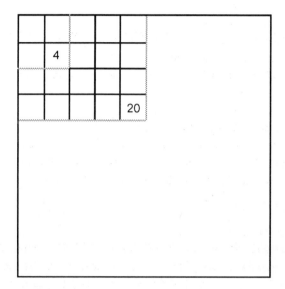

After they have completed a few examples, discuss with the children how every small square on the 10 × 10 square represents the bottom right-hand corner of a rectangle. Ask the children to complete the 10 × 10 square. Some children may need to make more rectangles, while others may be able to continue without having to draw the rectangles.

As the children complete the square, ask them to take note of any patterns they find which help them to fill in the square quickly.

When completed, the square can be mounted on card and laminated. Show the children how to use their squares to find all the multiplication facts to 10 × 10. They can keep the completed squares for further work on patterns and for reference purposes.

Suggestion(s) for extension

Look at some of the patterns on the multiplication square. Identify the square numbers. The children should immediately notice how they form the diagonal of the square.

Ask them to shade different multiples and look at the resulting patterns.

Cut up a multiplication square as a jigsaw and ask the children to fit it back together as quickly as possible. This is made even harder by preparing a jigsaw multiplication grid with some of the numbers missing.

Suggestion(s) for support

Build up the square slowly. Begin with rectangles with only 1, 2 or 3 rows. The children may need to count the number of small squares in each rectangle. Then spend time discussing how the rectangles fit on to the large 10 × 10 square.

Assessment opportunities

Note the children's ability to draw the rectangles representing the multiplication facts. Do they recognise that they do not need to draw rectangles for every fact? Observe how confident they are filling in the square. Are they unsure of many of the multiplication facts? The enthusiasm and pace at which the children work on this activity will give you clues as to how familiar they are with multiplication facts.

Opportunities for IT

The children could use a graphics package to make a personal copy of the multiplication square for lamination and later use. They might use different colours or fonts to highlight particular tables or patterns, to make the square easier to use. To save time you could create a master 10 × 10 grid and the children could use this as a starting point for their own squares.

Display ideas

The children can keep their own copies of the multiplication square, but it is a good idea to have a large copy on display in a prominent position in the classroom. At odd moments in the day ask the children multiplication questions. Encourage them to use the square if they cannot recall the answer.

CODE CAPERS

To be able to use multiplication facts to 10 × 10.

†† *Individuals.*

🕐 *30–40 minutes.*

Previous skills/knowledge needed

The children need to be familiar with the multiplication facts to 10 × 10 and should understand the idea of a coded message.

Preparation

Make copies of photocopiable worksheets 128 and 129 for each child.

Resources needed

Copies of photocopiable worksheets 128 and 129 for each child, pencils, paper, calculators (optional), 10 × 10cm blank squared grids (for the extension activity).

What to do

Start by giving each child a copy of the code square on photocopiable worksheet 128. The following introductory activity will get the children familiar with using the code square. Read out the instructions at the top of the page and go through the given example of a coded message. Make sure the children understand that they have to find the correct place on the square to identify the letters in the message.

Ask the children to decode the message written at the bottom of the sheet. Then ask them to write a short message of their own. They must then convert this into code using the square and write it on a piece of paper. Give the children time to make their coded messages and then ask each of them to give their message to the person next to them to work out.

Now distribute copies photocopiable sheet 129. Once again read out the instructions. This time the children have to use their knowledge of the multiplication facts to find the letters in the code. Go through some examples with the children: $5 \times 11 = 55$ which is Q. Then give them time to complete the three messages. Ask them to plan their coded message carefully for others in the class to decipher.

Suggestion(s) for extension

Give the children a blank 10 × 10 square. Ask them to fill it in by placing the letters A to Z in various spaces on the square and then writing the numbers from 1 to 100 in the blanks as on photocopiable sheet 128. Now they can make their own coded messages based on multiplication.

Suggestion(s) for support

Assist the children with reading the instructions on the first sheet. Help them to decode the message given and prepare some simple words in advance for them to decode too.

The second activity could be introduced gradually. If the children are unsure of the multiplication facts they could use calculators or their multiplication squares to help them to find the answers.

Assessment opportunities

Observe how quickly and confidently the children complete the messages written on photocopiable page 129. Can they recall all the multiplication facts to 10 × 10? Do they need to refer to a multiplication square or use a calculator? When devising their own messages can they easily identify multiplication sentences to match the number squares? The answers to these questions will help you in assessing how well the children know and recall the multiplication facts to 10 × 10.

Display ideas

Draw the code square on large squared paper an stick it on to card. Put the children's coded messages into a book

---

Code capers

Name _____ Date _____

You can use this secret code square to send messages to your friends.

On the square below are some letters. Find the one you want and then write down the number that *should be* in that square. For example, the letter C would be 9 and the letter O would be 100.

So the word 'code' would be 9/100/42/24.

1	G	3	R	5	6	7	8	C	10
11	U	13	14	15	K	17	Y	19	20
L	22	23	E	25	26	27	28	29	30
31	32	33	34	V	N	37	38	39	J
41	D	43	44	45	46	47	48	S	50
51	W	53	54	Q	A	57	58	59	60
61	62	H	F	65	66	67	68	69	70
71	P	73	74	75	76	T	78	79	M
B	82	83	X	85	86	87	88	89	90
Z	92	93	94	95	I	97	98	99	O

▲ What does this message say?
80/56/77/63/49   96/49   64/12/36

▲ Write a message to a friend. Remember to leave a gap between each word.

---

entitled *Our secret messages*. Display this alongside the large code square and invite the children to work through it.

Find examples of other codes, such as Morse code, and display them alongside the children's work.

Reference to photocopiable sheets

Photocopiable sheet 129 includes a code square and presents an introductory activity. The message says: MATHS/IS/FUN.

Sheet 129 requires the children to work out multiplication facts to decipher coded messages using the code given on sheet 128. The messages are shown below. This sheet may be used for assessment purposes as evidence of the children's acquisition of multiplication facts.

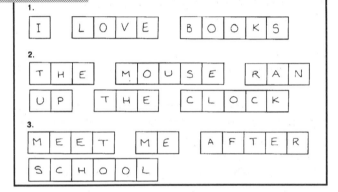

DISCOVER BY DIVIDING

To be able to recall number facts involving division and multiplication. To use the relationship between multiplication and division.

†† *Individuals.*

🕐 *30–45 minutes.*

Previous skills/knowledge needed

The children should have had experience of dividing two-digit numbers by one-digit numbers. They should appreciate the relationship between division and multiplication.

Key background information

Division is the inverse of multiplication; that is, it is multiplication in which the product is known and one of its factors is missing. For example: $4 = 8 \div 2$ means $4 \times 2 = 8$.

Preparation

Remind the children of the relationship between multiplication and division.

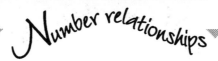
Make a copy of photocopiable worksheet 130 for each child.

Resources needed

A copy of photocopiable worksheet 130 for each child, coloured crayons, pencils, card , paper, calculators (optional).

What to do

This activity gives simple practice in using and reinforcing division facts.

Distribute copies of photocopiable sheet 130 to the children. Explain that they must imagine that they are pirates trying to find their buried treasure. As they travel along each path, they will come across circles with division sums inside. They have to work out each sum and follow the path with the correct answer. Tell them to continue doing this until they reach the spot where the treasure is buried, marking their route using a pencil. They should work out the answers to the division sums in their heads if they can. Encourage them to use their knowledge of multiplication facts by reminding them that division is the inverse of multiplication. For example, $20 \div 4 = 5$ because $4 \times 5 = 20$.

Suggestion(s) for extension

The same activity could be adapted, making the division sums more difficult.

If the children enjoyed the activity, suggest that they make their own treasure island worksheet. This will need careful planning and thought. A group of children could work on this together. The completed work could be coloured in, mounted on card and laminated for other children in the class to try.

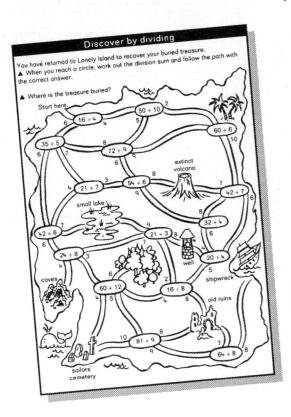

Suggestion(s) for support

Work on the first few sums with the children. Show them how to follow the correct route. Let them use counters, pegs or other mathematical resources to work out the answers, if necessary, or you may want to let them use a calculator. Continue to encourage them to predict first before checking.

Assessment opportunities

This activity will indicate how well the children know division and multiplication facts. Question the children as to how they worked out the answers. Are they using their knowledge of multiplication facts and seeing division as the inverse of multiplication?

Display ideas

Use the children's own work as a display in the classroom.

Mount their treasure maps on to card or make copies of them and put them out for other children to complete.

Reference to photocopiable sheet

Photocopiable worksheet 130 provides the map and division questions the children need to do the activity. You will need a copy for each child.

LINKS OF 20

To combine sets of numbers to make 20. To use knowledge of number facts to 20 to add a string of numbers.

†† *Whole class, then pairs, then whole class.*

🕓 *30 minutes.*

Previous skills/knowledge needed

The children should be able to recall addition facts to 10 from memory. The ability to add and subtract numbers mentally is an important part of the children's developing understanding of how numbers behave. Knowledge of the number facts to 20 will help them in further addition and subtraction work when dealing with larger numbers.

Preparation

Make copies of photocopiable sheet 131 for each pair of children.

Resources needed

Board or flipchart or large sheet of paper, marker pen, a copy of photocopiable worksheet 131 and two different-coloured pencils for each pair of children.

What to do

Begin the activity by asking the children to give you two numbers that add up to 10. Make a list of their examples on the board or a large sheet of paper.

Now ask them for two numbers which add up to 20. Again, make a list of their examples – beside the list for 10.

When you have finished, ask the children to look at both sets of number bonds. Through discussion, draw their attention to the repetition of the pattern of the bonds for 10 and 20:

1 + 9	11 + 9
2 + 8	12 + 8
3 + 7	13 + 7
4 + 6	14 + 6
5 + 5	15 + 5
6 + 4	16 + 4
7 + 3	17 + 3
8 + 2	18 + 2
9 + 1	19 + 1

Divide the children into pairs. Give each pair a copy of photocopiable worksheet 131 and two different-coloured pencils. Explain to the children that they are going to find sets of numbers which add up to 20; for example, 17 and 3, or 9 and 3 and 8. They must take turns and each player should use a different colour. When a player finds a suitable set of numbers he should link them together:

Any number can be used more than once. When no more sets can be found, the children can count how many each they have linked with their colour. The winner is the player with the most linked sets of numbers.

When each pair has finished get the group as a whole to compare how many sets of numbers they found. Did they all get the same number? Ask each pair to list their sets of numbers. Are they the same?

Now ask each pair if they can find, in their heads, the total of *all* the numbers on the sheet. When they have an answer, get them to explain how they found it. Did each pair in the group get the same answer? Did they use different methods to find the total? Encourage the children to explain their methods.

Suggestion(s) for extension

Encourage the children to work on sets of numbers which add up to 50 or 100. Point out links with number bonds to 20. For example: 9 + 3 + 8 = 20 and 19 + 13 + 18 = 50. These children could try to make their own activity sheet for other pairs to do.

Suggestion(s) for support

Spend more time revising the numbers bonds to 10, and then to 20. Make a worksheet similar to the photocopiable page, but only include numbers less than 10. Then the children can find sets of numbers which add up to 10.

Assessment opportunities

Observe the children working in their pairs. How familiar is each child with the number bonds to 20? Do they always choose combinations involving two numbers, or are they able to use three or more numbers together?

Watch closely when the children work out the sum of all the numbers and listen to their explanations. Do they use their combinations of 20 to group the numbers, or do they add each number separately? Can they follow the explanations of the others in the group.

By observing the children at work, you should be able to assess how well they are able to combine numbers in their heads to make a total of 20. Listening to them will tell you what mental methods they have used to add all the numbers and whether they have made use of the sets of 20 to obtain the total.

Reference to photocopiable sheet

Photocopiable page 131 provides a selection of numbers in which children have to find sets adding up to 20. The children will need one copy between two.

ADDING MULTIPLES OF 10

To be able to see the pattern when adding multiples of 10 and to add mentally multiples of 10 to any number.

†† *Small group of four to six children.*

🕐 *30–40 minutes.*

Previous skills/knowledge needed

The children should be familiar with numbers over 100 and should be able to add in 10s confidently – 10, 20, 30, 40 and so on.

Key background information

Seeing the patterns formed by adding 10s will help the children to acquire the skill of adding mentally multiples of 10 to any number.

The calculator is a useful aid for this kind of work as the children can investigate more easily number patterns and relationships. A constant addition function is set up on a calculator by entering:

①⓪⊕⊕＝＝ ...

or

①⓪⊕＝＝ ...

Preparation

Cut out four or five strips of squared paper (2 squares × 15 or 16 squares) for every child.

Resources needed

Board or flipchart or large sheet of paper, marker pen, strips of squared paper, pencils, calculators.

What to do

Ask the children to switch on their calculators. The display will show 0. Ask them to keep adding 10. Check if they know how to set up a constant function on their calculators. If not, explain this to them. Ask them to explain what happens when they add 10 continuously. Make sure they continue adding 10 past 100 so they see that the pattern begins again. Record the pattern on the board or a large sheet of paper. Draw their attention to the 0 (zero) in the units place.

Now ask them to start with 2 in the display. What do they think will happen if they keep adding 10 now? Ask them to try it and see. What do they notice? Again, draw their attention to the digit in the units place.

Ask them to choose another start number and continue adding 10. This time they can record the pattern of numbers on one of the strips of squared paper. The growing numbers are recorded in the spaces as follows:

17	27	37	47	57	67	77	87
...	117	127	137	147	157	167	177

Ask the children if they can completely fill the strip without having to use their calculators. Discuss with them what they have discovered.

Next, ask them to start with 0 in the display and keep adding 20. Discuss what happens. Let the children choose another start number and continue adding 20, recording their results on another strip of squared paper. Once again, get them to explain what is happening and continue the pattern without the aid of the calculator.

Now draw the group together, and discuss what they have discovered about adding 10 or 20 to a number. Can they predict what would happen if they added 30 to a number, or 40? They can use more strips to record what they find when they try this.

Choose a start number and tell it to the children. Then ask each child in turn to add 10. Ensure that this is within the capabilities of all the children in the group. Now ask one of them to choose a start number. Tell the next person to add 10, the following person to add 20, the person after that to add 10 and so on. The children can decide how long to continue, or the penalty if a mistake is made.

Suggestion(s) for extension

A further activity might be to explore the effect of adding 5 to the calculator display starting from 0. The children could also look at the effect of adding 2 or 4.

Suggestion(s) for support

Make some partially completed number strips. Fill in some of the numbers, leaving other spaces blank. Ask the children to complete these strips. Concentrate on adding 10 only to a number. Try putting different start numbers on the number tracks and ask the children to keep adding 10, using the calculator. You could also get them to 'jump' in 10s along a number line. Discuss the fact that the units, or 1s, do not change as you add/jump along to whereas the 10s increase by one each time. Ask questions such as: 'If I start with 7 and keep adding 10, will 25 appear in my list of answers?' Spend some time discussing what happens when we add 10 to a number such as 93 or 98. Are the children confident counting beyond 100?

Assessment opportunities

The completed strips will help you to assess whether a child is able to jump in 10s, 20s, 30s and so on from a starting number. However, it is discussion with the child that will tell you best how well he is able to add multiples of 10 to a number mentally. Ask him to explain what he has discovered:
▲ Start with 13 and add 30. What happens?
▲ Start with 81 and add 10. Now add 30. What happens?
▲ What if we start with 55 and add 60?
▲ Can you work with larger numbers? Add 40 to 366. What answer do you get?

Explaining what they have done and how they have done it is a valuable way of assessing how well the children have grasped the ideas involved in this activity.

Opportunities for IT

The children's use of calculators should be considered a part of their IT development. Setting up the constant function on the calculator will help them to appreciate the necessity for accurate keying and the following of a procedure. In actual fact, the calculator models the tens number system and the children are creating a system which models the repeated addition or subtraction of a number.

Also encourage the children to look at their answers and check them for accuracy, relating the result to the expected answer and the keys pressed. As with computers, calculators depend on accurate keying and the correct sequences of commands to create accurate results.

9 AND 99

To be able to add 9 and 99 to a number quickly. To be able to subtract 9 and 99 from a number quickly.

†† *Large group, then pairs.*

🕒 *45–60 minutes.*

Previous skills/knowledge needed

The children should be able to add and subtract two numbers. They should also be able to count on and back in 10s and 100s from any number.

Preparation

For each pair of children, copy the game board on sheet 132 directly or mount it on to card. If possible, laminate the copies or cover them with clear adhesive plastic. Each pair will also need a copy of photocopiable sheet 133 made directly on to card or mounted and then cut up into individual cards.

Resources needed

Board or flipchart or large sheet of paper, marker pen, paper, pencils. For each pair of children you will need: a game board and a set of operation cards (see 'Preparation' above), a dice, two different-coloured counters, a calculator.

What to do

Write a list of numbers on the board or on a large sheet of paper so that they are visible to all the children. An example could be: 5, 12, 9, 26, 53 and 97. Ask the children to add 10 to each of the numbers and call out the answers.

Write a new list of larger numbers, say: 104, 263, 129, 483, 315 and 247. Ask the children to add, in their heads, 10 to each of these numbers. They may write them down if they wish. Ask them to explain how they did it. If necessary, help them with the place value language of hundreds, tens, units and zero. Discuss the patterns that result when we add 10 to a number.

Do the same exercise, but this time adding 100 to the numbers. Once again, discuss the methods used.

Now tell the children that there is a quick way of adding 9 to a number, using what they know about adding 10. Explain that to add 9 to a number, we can add 10 first, then subtract 1.

Ask them to try this with the first set of numbers. Go through all the examples. As the children add 9 to each number, ask them to explain what they are doing. They should respond that: 'To add 9 to 26 we add 10 to make 36, and

then subtract 1 to make 35.' Can they explain why this method works?

Try the same activity, but this time adding 99 to the numbers. Explain that to add 99 to a number we can add 100 first, and then subtract 1. So, to add 99 to 315, we add 100 to make 415, then subtract 1 to make 414. Encourage the children to try some examples of their own.

They could write a list of numbers for their partner to work on:

Number	+9
7	16
29	
63	
14	
72	
128	

Number	+99
6	105
103	
75	
264	
18	
377	

Stop the group when each child has worked through several examples. Write out a new list of numbers and ask the children to *subtract* 10 from each of the numbers. As before, discuss with them the methods they use. Ask them if they can think of a quick way of subtracting 9 from each of the numbers. Some of them will see that a similar method can be used for subtracting 9 as was used for adding 9. If necessary, explain that to subtract 9 we subtract 10 first, then *add* 1. Let the children try this with some of the examples already given.

Go through the same procedure to establish subtracting 99 from the list of numbers. Re-emphasise that to subtract 99 from a number we subtract 100 first, and then add 1. For example, to subtract 99 from 853 we subtract 100 to make 753, then add 1 to make 754.

Again, the children can write out a list of numbers for their partners to try:

Number	–9
23	14
45	
72	
39	
89	
84	

Number	–99
352	253
198	
403	
226	
949	
646	

When the children have worked through several examples they can play the '9 and 99' board game. This is played in pairs and will give the children practice using the methods they have just covered.

Distribute a game board and a set of operation cards to each pair. They will also need a dice and a counter each. Tell them to shuffle the cards and put the pack face down in the middle of the table. Explain that they must take turns to throw the dice and move their counters along the track. To jump over a fence a player must take the top card from the pack and answer the sum correctly before continuing. They may use a calculator to check their answers. If a player is incorrect, she must return to the square from which she started her move. If a player answers correctly she can continue. The card should be returned to the bottom of the pack. The first player to reach the finishing line is the winner. Let the children play the game a few times. Different cards could be added to the pack to make it more varied.

Suggestion(s) for extension
Extend the numbers to add and subtract to 999. For example, try asking the children to add 199 to a number, or subtracting 599.

Ask them if they can think up a quick way of adding or subtracting 8 or 88. Ask them to explain their method.

Suggestion(s) for support
First, ensure that the children can add and subtract 10 and 100 from numbers easily. If necessary, spend time counting on and backwards in 10s and then 100s.

Illustrate the quick way of adding and subtracting 9 and 99 with the use of structural apparatus, such as base 10 equipment. Make sure that the children can see that adding 10 and subtracting 1 is the same as adding 9.

Assessment opportunities
Question individual children about the methods they use to add and subtract 10 and 100.

Observe them adding and subtracting 9 and 99, do they find the answers quickly?

Observe pairs of children playing the game. Note whether they are able to work out the answers quickly. Do they need a calculator?

Display ideas
Make a poster for the classroom entitled 'Quick ways to add and subtract 9 and 99'. Explain and illustrate the methods described above.

Reference to photocopiable sheets
Photocopiable sheet 132 is the board for the game used in this activity. Photocopiable sheet 133 offers a set of operation cards to be used when playing the game.

FACTORS

To be able to identify factors of numbers up to 40. To look at the total number of factors of particular numbers.

†† *Pairs.*

🕑 *45–60 minutes.*

Previous skills/knowledge needed
The children should be familiar with multiplication facts to 10×10. Also, they will need to know some of the properties of numbers such as odds and evens, square and rectangular numbers.

Key background information
In this activity the children will be introduced to factors and asked to find the factors of the numbers from 1 to 40. Factors are the only natural numbers that will divide exactly into a given number without remainders. The factors of 10, for example, are: 1, 2, 5 and 10. In looking at the total number of factors for each number, it will be found that those numbers with only two factors make up the set of prime numbers: 2, 3, 5, 7, 11, 13, 17, 19, 23, 29, 31, 37. Those numbers with three factors are the squares of prime numbers: $4 = 2^2$, $9 = 3^2$ and $25 = 5^2$. Numbers with four factors are all rectangular numbers. Those numbers with an odd number of factors are the square numbers: 1, 4, 9, 16, 25 and 36.

Preparation
Discuss with the children any previous work they may have done on square and rectangular numbers.

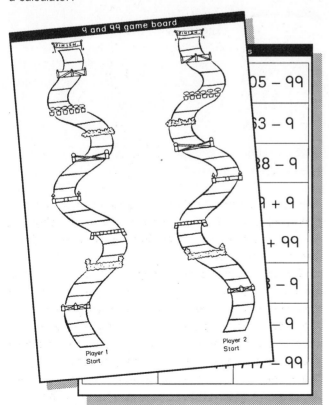

9 and 99 game board

FINISH

Player 1 Start

Player 2 Start

05 – 99

63 – 9

88 – 9

9 + 9

+ 99

8 – 9

– 9

– 99

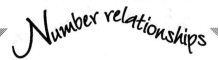

Resources needed

Centimetre squared paper, lined paper, pencils, Unifix cubes, calculators (optional).

What to do

Give each pair of children some centimetre squared paper, a piece of lined paper, a pencil and some Unifix cubes. Begin the activity by asking them to take 24 cubes and to arrange them in a rectangular layer in as many different ways as possible. Tell them to record each arrangement on the squared paper and to write down the number of rows and columns of each rectangle:

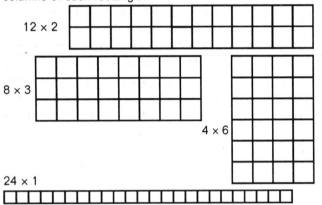

When they have done this, tell the children that 1, 2, 3, 4, 6, 8, 12 and 24 are all 'factors' of 24; that is, the only numbers that divide exactly into 24 without remainders.

Ask them to try the same activity with 16 cubes. This time they may not need the cubes and may be able to draw the arrangements straight on to the squared paper. Once again, point out that 1, 2, 4, 8 and 16 are known as the factors of 16.

Tell the children that they are going to find the factors of all the numbers from 1 to 40 and that they are to use the lined paper to record what they find. They can use cubes or squared paper, if they wish, to help them. Tell them to set out their work in three coloumns. They should write the factors for each number in the middle column headed 'Factors'. It is important that they write the factors in the correct order, as shown below. They should write the total number of factors in the right-hand column. Show the children how to do the first few:

Number	Factors	Total number of factors
1	1	1
2	1, 2	2
3	1, 3	2
4	1, 2, 4	3

Encourage each pair to work together. Each child could work on alternate numbers, or one could take the numbers from 1 to 20, the other 21 to 40. You could simplify the recording of this activity by ruling and heading the columns on a sheet of lined paper yourself and using this as a master sheet for photocopying.

When the page is complete, ask them if they have noticed any patterns among the factors. They may notice that every number has a factor of 1 and itself, and that 2 is a factor of all the even numbers. Discuss this with them.

Draw the children's attention to the total number of factors for each number from 1 to 40 by asking questions such as:
▲ Is there anything significant about how many factors a number has?
▲ Look at the numbers with an odd number of factors. Have you seen these numbers before?

Tell them to list the numbers which have only two factors. These factors are always 1 and the number itself. Explain that these numbers are called 'prime numbers'. Then ask the children to list the numbers with three and four factors and encourage them to look for patterns. The children should write about any relationships they can find between the numbers and their factors.

Finally, ask them if they can predict higher numbers which would have a certain number of factors. For example, 81, being a square number, should have an odd number of factors.

Suggestion(s) for extension

Suggest that the children use a calculator to find the factors of numbers up to 100.

Encourage them to predict numbers with three and four factors and ask them to explain their reasoning.

Suggestion(s) for support

Spend more time exploring the factors of numbers from 1 to 20. Make the rectangular arrangements for each number using pegs and a pegboard.

Ensure that the children have understood the link between factors and multiplication. For example, 20 is made up of four 5s, therefore 4 and 5 are factors of 20.

Assessment opportunities

If the children can find the factors of the numbers from 1 to 40 fairly quickly, without having to draw each rectangular arrangement, this offers evidence that they are familiar with multiplication facts and are able to recognise the link between factors and multiplication.

In discussion with the children, consider the following:
▲ How easily do the children identify the square numbers and the prime numbers?
▲ Can they predict which numbers will have a particular number of factors?
▲ Have they discovered any new patterns?

FACTOR TREES

To be able to break down a number into its factors, using multiplication facts.

†† *Small group of four to six children.*

🕐 *45–60 minutes.*

Previous skills/knowledge needed

The children should know multiplication facts to 10 × 10. They should have some experience of finding factors of numbers and know that prime numbers have only two factors – the number itself and 1.

Key background information

Numbers that are not prime are called 'composite numbers'. Composite numbers can be split, by multiplication, again and again until we reach prime numbers. A factor tree can illustrate this.

For example, if we take the number 30. This can be reduced in the following ways:

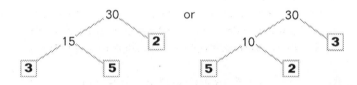

The ends of the branches are the 'prime factors' of 30; that is, 3, 5 and 2 are all prime numbers: 3 × 5 × 2.

The factorisation of a composite number can produce several different trees for that number, but the prime factors at the ends of the branches will be the same.

Preparation

If necessary, remind the children about factors and prime numbers.

Make copies of photocopiable sheet 134 for the extension activity.

Resources needed

Large sheets of paper, marker pens, calculators, multiplication squares, copies of photocopiable worksheet 134 for extension activity.

What to do

Tell the children that they are going to build 'family trees' for some numbers. Start by writing the number 30 at the top of a large sheet of paper. Explain to the children how 30 can be split into two branches representing two of the factors of 30.

Draw the two branches on the sheet and write the numbers 10 and 3 at the ends:

Show the children how the 10 can be split into two branches also and write the multiplication sentence:

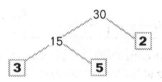

5 × 2 × 3

Tell the children that they have reached the end of the tree and point out that the numbers at the bottom are all prime numbers. If necessary, remind the children that primes can only be split into themselves and 1. Show them how these prime numbers make 30 when multiplied together and, therefore, that 5, 2 and 3 are the 'prime factors' of 30.

Tell the children that there is another way to draw a tree for 30 and write 30 on the reverse side of the sheet of paper. Can any of the children tell you how to begin the tree in a different way? Continue the diagram:

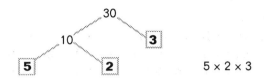

Draw their attention to the fact that you have reduced 30 to the same three prime numbers: 3, 5 and 2.

Ask the children in the group to draw factor trees for the numbers 10, 20, 40, 60 and 80. They could work together, allocating different numbers to each member of the group. Most children will be able to split multiples of 10.

Then the group can go on to explore other numbers. Encourage them to use a calculator to check that multiplying the prime factors will give the original composite number.

Suggestion(s) for extension

Let the children build factor trees for larger, three-digit numbers, beginning with multiples of 10 such as 150 or 200. A group of children could work together on one number, finding all the possible ways of building the trees.

Give the children some examples of factor trees which have numbers missing, such as those on photocopiable worksheet 134. Encourage the children to find the missing numbers.

Suggestion(s) for support

The children can use multiplication squares (see page 38) to help them identify the factors. Spend more time working on multiples of 10 as these are generally the easiest numbers to split. Then have the children work on smaller numbers such as 15, 9, 24 and 12.

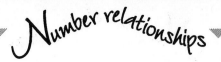
Assessment opportunities

The children's own diagrams of the factor trees will provide evidence of their ability to break down a number into its factors. Note how confidently they work with larger numbers.

Try to identify those children who are hesitant in their ability to recall the factors of multiples of 10 or the smaller numbers. Do they need more experience and activities exploring multiplication?

Display ideas

The factor trees of particular numbers can be drawn on to large sheets of paper or card and mounted as posters for the classroom.

One idea could be to write the original number at the bottom of the sheet and draw branches with the factors at the end:

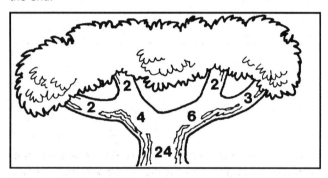

Reference to photocopiable sheet

Photocopiable worksheet 134 is an extension activity and provides examples of factor trees with missing numbers. The answers are:

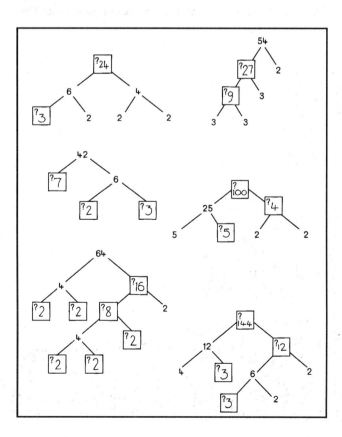

FIBONACCI NUMBERS

To recognise and investigate Fibonacci numbers.

†† *Pairs.*

🕐 *30–45 minutes.*

Previous skills/knowledge needed

The children should have some past experience using Cuisenaire rods and be able to add two- and three-digit numbers.

Key background information

The number pattern generated by this activity is known as the 'Fibonacci sequence'.

Fibonacci was an Italian mathematician who lived during the 12th century. Each term of his sequence is found by finding the sum of two consecutive terms to give the next term. So: $1 + 1 = 2$, $1 + 2 = 3$, $2 + 3 = 5$ and so on. The first eight numbers in the sequence are: 1, 1, 2, 3, 5, 8, 13, 21.

The sequence appears in nature where it models certain natural phenomena such as the population growth in bees and rabbits, and the development of the spiral in a snail's shell. There are many reference books which will help the teacher to investigate the numbers further.

Resources needed

For each pair of children you will need: Cuisenaire rods, squared paper, pencils, plain paper, a calculator.

What to do

Distribute the squared paper. Ask the children to make the number 3 using only the 1 and 2 Cuisenaire rods. How many different ways can they do it? They should produce the following arrangements:

You may want to discuss whether $2 + 1$ and $1 + 2$ are the same arrangement. (For the purposes of this activity, consider them to be different.)

Now ask the children to make the number 4 using only the '1' and '2' rods. Give them time to put together the rods, then ask them to record the arrangements they can make on the squared paper.

Ask the children to record their results on plain paper in a table such as:

1	1 way
2	2 ways
3	3 ways...

When they have filled in the table, ask them if they can see the pattern. Can they predict how many ways there are of making 7? What about 10 or 15? (They may need to use a calculator as the numbers become quite large.) Can they explain the pattern?

Finally, tell the children the name of the sequence – the Fibonacci sequence.

Suggestion(s) for extension

The children could try one of the problems which appeared in a book by Fibonacci himself. Versions of this problem can be found in numerous mathematics books.

A pair of rabbits at one month old are too young to have baby rabbits, but when they are two months old they will have a pair of rabbits, and every month after they will produce another pair of babies. Each pair of rabbits does the same. How many rabbits will there be at the end of six months? (13 pairs.) One year? (233 pairs.) The numbers of pairs each month generate the Fibonacci sequence – see below.

Suggestion(s) for support

You may need to spend some time discussing with the children how the numbers in the sequence grow. Once they understand how each number is generated, let them use a calculator to find the next six terms.

Ask them to write out the sequence and find the difference between each consecutive pair of numbers. They will discover that the same sequence appears again.

Assessment opportunities

Ask the children to show you their diagrams recording what they did. Discuss their work with them.

Ask questions such as:
▲ Did you discover the pattern of numbers yourself?
▲ Can you explain the sequence to me?
▲ How can you predict the number of ways to make 12?

Establish from their responses whether they have understood how the numbers in the Fibonacci sequence grow.

Opportunities for IT

Children who have worked on a spreadsheet, might like to experiment with setting up the Fibonnaci sequence. The spreadsheet might look like this:

A	B	gives		
1	0			
2	1	1		
3	B1+B2	1		
4	B2+B3	2		
5	B3+B4	3		
6	B4+B5	5		
7	B5+B6	8		

Note that a formula can only be used once the first two numbers have been entered as the two consecutive starting numbers.

Display ideas

Research into the Fibonacci sequence as it occurs in nature and architecture and display the information along with the children's work.

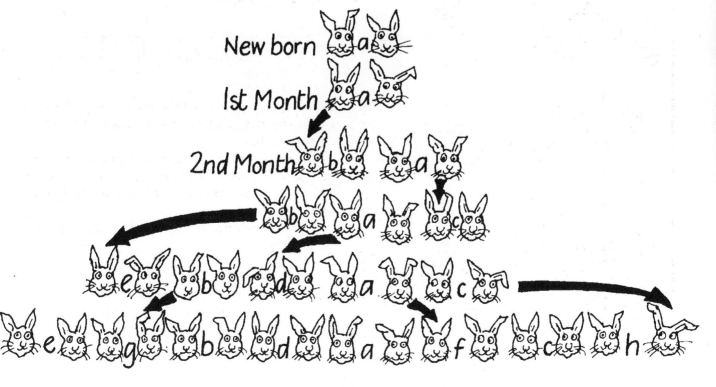

New born

1st Month

2nd Month

SIEVING OUT PRIMES

To identify prime numbers below 100 using the 'Sieve of Eratosthenes'.

✝✝ *Whole class or individuals, then whole class or group discussion.*

🕐 *30–45 minutes.*

Previous skills/knowledge needed

The children should be familiar with multiples and factors of natural numbers.

Key background information

Any number which can be divided only by itself and 1 is called a 'prime number'. For example, the number 13 is prime as it has only itself and 1 as factors: 1 × 13 = 13. It is not usual to regard 1 as a prime number as it only has one factor, itself! Two is the lowest, and only even, prime number.

The existence of prime numbers has been known for thousands of years. They have always interested mathematicians, partly because they do not fall into any recognisable pattern. In the 3rd century BC a Greek mathematician, Eratosthenes, devised a method of identifying the prime numbers, known as the 'Sieve of Eratosthenes'.

The activity described below takes the children through this process of eliminating particular numbers, using a 100 square, so that only the primes are left.

Preparation

Amend the blank 100 square on photocopiable sheet 120 to a completed 1–100 square. Use this as a master copy from which to make a 100 square for each child.

Resources needed

A completed 100 square for each child, coloured pencils.

What to do

Provide each child with a 100 square and some coloured pencils. Give the children specific instructions (set out below) as to how to shade in the different numbers. They should pick up the idea quickly and be able to continue on their own with the numbers up to 100. They may wish to use the constant function of their calculators to help them to keep the multiplication pattern correct.

▲ Cross out the first square containing the number 1.

▲ Put a circle around 2 and then shade every multiple of 2 on the 100 square.

▲ Using a different colour, put a circle around the number 3 and then shade every multiple of 3.

▲ Do the same for number 5 and its multiples, then number 7 and its multiples.

Ask the children to look at the numbers not shaded or with a circle round, for example: 11, 13, 17, 19 and 23. Do the children think that these numbers are multiples? If not, can they tell you what is special about them? Ask them to identify more numbers that are not multiples.

Then let them continue with the sieve activity by circling the next blank number (11) and shading any of its multiples not already coloured in. They should continue like this with every subsequent blank number and its multiples until every number is ringed (the primes) or shaded.

When the children have finished they should have circled all the prime numbers below 100. The numbers shaded in are their multiples. (See diagram on page 50.)

You could discuss the following questions with the class or group:

▲ Have you noticed that all the primes, with the exception of 2, are odd numbers?

▲ 'Prime numbers, with the exception of 2 and 3, precede or follow a multiple of 6.' Is this always the case?

▲ Can you find, say, two primes which total 78? Can you continue to find three primes? Four primes? What about for a total of 52?

▲ Can you find different combinations of three primes which, when added together, will give you a total of 53?

▲ Can you devise a puzzle based on the prime numbers?

Suggestion(s) for extension

The children could investigate 'twin primes'. These are prime numbers such as 11 and 13, which are only two apart. Are there any others?

Some primes are the sum of two square numbers. Can the children find any, for example, $53 = 7^2 + 2^2$?

Suggestion(s) for support

Encourage the children to use cubes or pegs and a pegboard to make rectangular arrangements of the smaller, natural numbers. They should discover quickly that the prime numbers can only be made into one rectangular arrangement, for example:

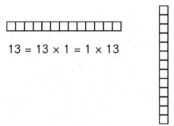

$$13 = 13 \times 1 = 1 \times 13$$

Assessment opportunities

Observe the children filling in the 100 square. Can they identify multiples of numbers quickly and confidently?

Discuss the finished 100 square with them and ask them about what they have been doing. Can they explain what a prime number is? You will need to decide whether they understand how the sieve works.

Display ideas

Illustrate the prime numbers on a large hundred square. Display this along with the work that the children have done. Encourage them to find out about Eratosthenes and to try to explain how

his 'sieve' works. All this work could form part of a wider topic covering Ancient Greek mathematicians or special numbers.

Reference to photocopiable sheet

Photocopiable sheet 120 provides a large 100 square to be completed and copied for use in this activity.

INDEX NOTATION

To use and recognise index notation, including numbers to the power 2 and 3, and to be able to identify cube numbers.

†† *Small groups of four or five children.*

🕐 *45 minutes.*

Previous skills/knowledge needed

The children should know multiplication facts and be able to multiply a two-digit number by a one-digit number. Also, they need to be familiar with square numbers.

Key background information

When a number is multiplied by itself, the result is the square of the number. For example: $4 \times 4 = 16$. This can be written in an abbreviated form as 4^2 (4 squared).

If a number is multiplied by itself three times, the result is the cube of the number. For example: $4 \times 4 \times 4 = 64$. This can be written as 4^3 (4 cubed).

This shorthand way of writing 4×4 and $4 \times 4 \times 4$ is known as 'index notation'. When a number is multiplied by itself n times, the result is the nth power of the number. So 5^3 can be referred to as '5 to the power 3' ($5 \times 5 \times 5$).

Using index notation it is possible to record very large numbers.

Preparation

To simplify this activity you may wish to use ruled paper to prepare two grids as shown below, and then copy them for each child:

Cube number	Multiplication sentence	Index notation	

Square number	Multiplication sentence	Index notation	

Otherwise the children can organise their work for themselves in a similar way using ruled paper.

For the extension activity you will need a set of bingo cards and call numbers for each group of four children. Cut these from copies of photocopiable sheet 135. The bingo cards are best copied or mounted on to card and laminated.

Resources needed

Cuisenaire rods, base 10 equipment, ruled paper or preprepared grids, a large piece of paper, a marker pen, centimetre squared paper, pencils, calculators, a set of bingo cards, 80 counters and the call numbers for extension work (one set per group of four children).

What to do

Ask the children to draw the first four square numbers on the centimetre squared paper. They should write a multiplication sentence underneath each one:

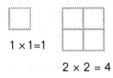

$1 \times 1 = 1$

$2 \times 2 = 4$

$3 \times 3 = 9$

$4 \times 4 = 16$

Explain to them that square numbers can be written in a special way and that instead of writing $4 \times 4 = 16$ we can write 4^2. Tell them that this is read as '4 squared', or '4 to the power 2'. What do they think will be the shorthand way of writing the fifth square number? Ask them to write all the square numbers they know in this way.

Now take a large sheet of paper and write on it '2^3'. Show it to the children and ask them if anyone can guess what it means. They may be able to make the link between this notation and that used for the square numbers. If not, explain to them that 2^3 is a way of writing $2 \times 2 \times 2$: the number has been multiplied by itself three times. Ask them to work this out. If necessary, explain to them that they can break the problem down by finding 2×2 and them multiplying the answer by 2. So, $2 \times 2 = 4$, and $4 \times 2 = 8$. Therefore, $2^3 = 2 \times 2 \times 2 = 8$.

Turn your sheet of paper over and write on it 3^3. Ask the children to read this number out and explain to you what it means. Tell them to work out the number that is '3 to the power 3'. You may have to re-emphasise the meaning of 'power' to the children. At this point you could introduce the idea of cubic numbers if the children have not already had experience of them. Give each child some ruled paper or the preprepared grids. Ask them to list the first ten square and cube numbers, with their matching multiplication sentences and index notation. The children should have access to calculators to help them with the larger numbers. Ask the children to discuss their findings with each other, checking their results.

The children's completed lists should look like this:

Square number	Multiplication sentence	Index notation
1	1×1	1^2
4	2×2	2^2
9	3×3	3^2
16	4×4	4^2
25	5×5	5^2
36	6×6	6^2
49	7×7	7^2
64	8×8	8^2
81	9×9	9^2
100	10×10	10^2

Cube number	Multiplication sentence	Index notation
1	$1 \times 1 \times 1$	1^3
8	$2 \times 2 \times 2$	2^3
27	$3 \times 3 \times 3$	3^3
64	$4 \times 4 \times 4$	4^3
125	$5 \times 5 \times 5$	5^3
216	$6 \times 6 \times 6$	6^3
343	$7 \times 7 \times 7$	7^3
512	$8 \times 8 \times 8$	8^3
729	$9 \times 9 \times 9$	9^3
1000	$10 \times 10 \times 10$	10^3

Suggestion(s) for extension

The children can go on to play 'Index bingo'. Give four children a bingo card each and some counters. One child (or the teacher) picks out the 'call numbers' (which are written in index notation) from an opaque bag and reads them aloud. For example, for '2^3', the child would say, 'Two to the power three.' The children all look to see if they have that number (8) on their board, and if so cover it with a counter. The winner is the first player to cover a line of four numbers correctly, either horizontally, vertically or diagonally.

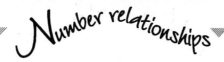

NUMBER PROPERTIES

To identify numbers by discovering their properties.
To use knowledge of primes, multiples, factors, square,
rectangular and cube numbers.

†† *Groups of four to six children.*

🕐 *30–45 minutes.*

Previous skills/knowledge needed
The children should know some of the properties of numbers such as primes, multiples and factors.

Preparation
Make a copy of photocopiable worksheet 136 for each child.
You will also need a set of 1–50 number cards for each group. These can be made from copies of photocopiable sheet 106. This sheet provides cards for the numbers 0 to 9. By adding digits, amend the 0 to 10, the 1 to 11 and so on on further copies, up to 50. If possible copy the sheets directly or mount them on to card and then laminate them or cover them with clear adhesive plastic to prolong their life.

Resources needed
A copy of photocopiable worksheet 136 for each child, a set of 1–50 number cards for each group, paper, pencils, calculators, centimetre squared paper, pegboards and pegs.

What to do
Give each child a copy of the 'number properties' worksheet and then tell the children that they are going to play a game. Shuffle the number cards and deal five to each child. Ask them each to write their numbers along the top row of the chart on the sheet. Then they should answer all the questions written down the left-hand side of the chart for the first number. Once this is done, they can go on to answer the list of questions for the other four numbers.

Suggestion(s) for support
Before distributing the preprepared grids, fill in parts of them. Ask the children to work up to the fifth row only.

Use Cuisenaire rods to show how the powers of 2 can be built up:

2 [ ]

2^2 [ ]

2^3 [ ]

Demonstrate the cube numbers using base 10 blocks.

Assessment opportunities
Can the children convert terms written in index notation back to the relevant multiplication sentence? Can they use Multibase blocks to build up the cube numbers?
Check the children's completed pages of square and cube numbers as evidence of their ability to identify and understand index notation.

Reference to photocopiable sheet
Photocopiable sheet 135 is a resource sheet to be used for the extension activity to play 'Index bingo'.

When all the children in the group have completed the questions for their five numbers, ask them to fold over the top row of the sheet, so that the top row numbers are out of sight. Then tell the children to swap sheets and try to guess the numbers from the top row of each other's tables. They should use the bottom row of the table in which to write their guesses. When all five spaces have been filled, let them turn back the top row. They score one point for each correct guess. The child with the most points is the winner.

Suggestion(s) for extension

Ask the children to select five numbers between 50 and 100 and find a mathematical property of each one. Tell them to make two lists: the numbers, and the properties muddled up. Then they can swap lists with their friends and try to map the numbers to the correct properties.

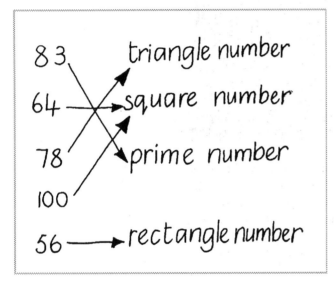

Suggestion(s) for support

Adapt the number properties table on the photocopiable worksheet to make it slightly easier to complete. Substitute questions such as:
▲ Is it less than 20?
▲ Is it more than 25?
▲ What multiplication table is it in?

Encourage the children to make a list of the square numbers less than 50 or all the primes and then to use such lists for reference to complete the questions.

Assessment opportunities

Observe one or two children filling in the table. Can they recall what they have been told about special numbers, such as primes and cube numbers? Do they need to use counters or diagrams to discover whether a number is square, triangular or cube? Can they work out factors and multiples of numbers easily or do they need support?

Display ideas

In groups, the children could make charts, each about one of the numbers. Help them to write the number in the centre and cover it in some way; for example, with a flap. Display the children's statements about its properties around it:

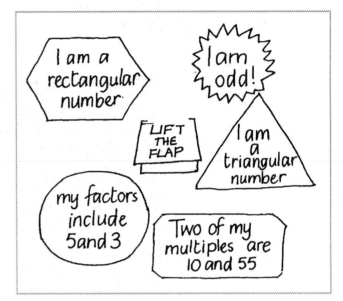

Reference to photocopiable sheets

Photocopiable worksheet 136 provides the children with nine questions to answer about five numbers between 1 and 50 chosen at random from a pack of 1–50 number cards (made from amended copies of photocopiable sheet 106). They can record their answers on the chart provided.

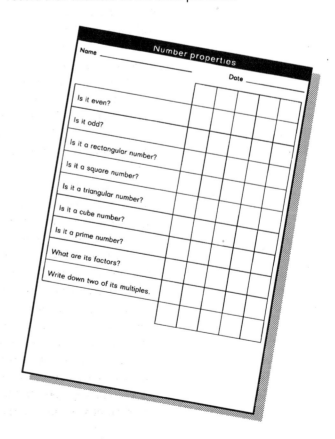

Calculations

In this chapter three interrelated aspects are addressed in turn: Operations, Problems and Checking. The major principle underlying all the activities in this chapter is the understanding and application of the processes involved. All the activities are designed to promote discussion to offer you the opportunity to assess the children's thinking and their conceptual understanding.

The first section of this chapter (pages 55–64) explores operations. Operations constitute a key element of mathematics and primary school children spend a great deal of time carrying out the basic operations in number. According to the Cockcroft Report (*Mathematics Counts*, DES, 1982, para. 298) the skills of written computation are founded on basic concepts which need to be developed through measurement, shopping, the use of structural apparatus and many other activities.

The activities in the second section (pages 64–71) offer children the chance to develop their computational skills to solve problems in a variety of contexts.

The children will become much more accurate in their work if they are encouraged to check the reasonableness (or appropriateness) of any results to calculations and problems they have produced. This can include looking at the context of the problem, using estimation and approximation and looking for pattern. The final section of this chapter (pages 71–78) suggests some of the ways children can be encouraged to check their results.

TWO FOR ONE

To be able to add two-digit numbers mentally by counting on.

†† *Individuals.*

🕐 *30 minutes.*

Previous skills/knowledge needed
The children should be able to add and subtract two-digit numbers.

Key background information
There are a variety of different ways to add on. In this activity the children are encouraged to take the number to the nearest ten first, but equally valid for 43 → 70 would be: 43 + 20 → 63 + 7 → 70, that is + 20 + 7.

Preparation
Write up the following grid of pairs of numbers on the board or flipchart, leaving a significant space between the columns:

Starting number	Additions	Finishing number
19		40
26		39
11		50
63		85
40		66
17		74
34		80
52		94
25		60
73		100

Resources needed
Board or flipchart or large sheet of paper, marker pen, paper, pencils, calculators, number lines (for support work).

What to do
Write a starting number, for example 43, and a finishing number, for example 70, on the board or flipchart or on a large piece of paper. Ask the children what two additions you could use to get from 43 to 70. Encourage them to take the starting number to the next ten first. In this case, it would be 'Add 7 to make 50.' The next addition is now made simpler as they need only decide what to add to 50 to reach 70. The children should be able to see that the second addition will be to 'Add 20': 43 + 7 → 50 + 20 → 70. Write + 7 + 20 between the starting and finishing numbers. Then explain to the children that although they can count on 7 from 43 to reach 50, and then count on 20 to reach the finishing number of 70, they could do a single addition that is the same. Ask them if they know what it is. If necessary, point out that + 7 + 20 is the same as + 27.

Try a few more examples together. Ask the children to explain the steps they are using to get from the starting to the finishing numbers.

Then suggest that they try the examples given on the board or flipchart. Ask them to copy the grid and then fill the centre column between each pair of numbers with two additions which take each of the starting numbers to the finishing number. The children can check their ideas on a calculator first.

The children can compare their results with their partners' to see if they got the same additions. Draw attention to any differences. For example, getting from 26 to 39 can be done by adding 4 and then 9: 26 + 4 → 30 + 9 → 39. However, some children might prefer to add 10 first and then 3: 26 + 10 → 36 + 3 → 39.

Suggestion(s) for extension
Adapt the grid to make the finishing numbers larger. Ask the children to include the *one* equivalent addition. For example: use a starting number of 19 and a finishing number of 120. The single addition would be + 101.

Suggestion(s) for support
Let the children use a number line to find the two 'jumps' that will get them to the finishing number. Spend time going through examples with them. Each time get them to illustrate their additions by drawing them on to the number line.

Instead of drawing a grid on the board, compile a similar chart on paper to photocopy for each child, substituting different numbers in the lists. Limit the finishing numbers to multiples of 10 initially, and then go on to use multiples of 5.

Assessment opportunities
Concentrate on one or two individual children. Question them carefully and listen to their explanations as to how they worked out what they needed to do to get from one number to another. Note their strategies. Their responses to your questions will give you some indication of how well they are able to count on to solve what is, basically, a subtraction sum; for example, 39 – 26 = ?

Display ideas

Display the children's work in a class book entitled *Two for one*. Include their written explanations of what they have done to change from one number to the other along with their examples.

SNAKES AND LADDERS

To be able to use the four operations confidently.
To be able to apply the inverse of an operation.
†† *Individuals.*
🕐 *30–40 minutes.*

Previous skills/knowledge needed

The children should be able to use the four operations with two-digit numbers. They should have a developing understanding of the relationships between the operations.

Key background information

The children should be encouraged, at an early stage in their number work, to recognise the links between the operations. They need to know, for example, that subtraction is the inverse of addition, and that division is the inverse of multiplication; that is, 'division undoes what is done by multiplication', and $7 + 3 = 10$ can be written also as $10 - 3 = 7$.

Preparation

Copy photocopiable sheet 137 directly, or mount the copies, on to card for each child. If possible, laminate them or cover

them with clear adhesive plastic. Then the snake and ladder on the page can be filled in by the children using water-based felt-tipped pens which can be wiped off easily. You may wish to make further paper copies of this sheet to amend for extension or support work, or for the children to use for display purposes.

Resources needed

'Snake and ladder' board for each child, water-based felt-tipped pens, paper, pencils, calculators (optional).

What to do

Give each child a copy of the 'Snake and ladder' board. Explain to them that they must choose a number between 1 and 10 and write this number at the bottom of the ladder and at the bottom of the snake. Then they should choose a number greater than 50, and write this number – the target number – at the top of the ladder and at the top of the snake.

Now they have to use the ladder to get from the bottom number to the target number. They should start by performing an addition, subtraction, multiplication or division operation on the starting number and write this, along with the answer, between the first and second rungs of the ladder. Tell them to keep performing different operations until they reach their target numbers.

The children will benefit at this stage from you working through an example with them:

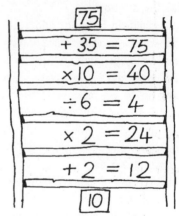

Now tell them that they have to reverse the process and get from their target number, down the snake, to the starting number:

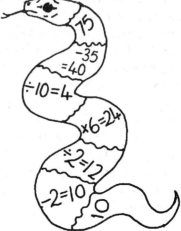

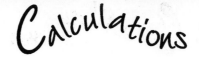

The children can use a calculator to check their progress as they go. Ask them to keep a record of their work.

Discuss with them how they used the operations written on the ladder to get down the snake. Let the children have several attempts at this activity using different starting and target numbers, wiping the board clean between each attempt.

Suggestion(s) for extension

Make several 'Snake and ladder' copies on paper. Put in the starter and target numbers along with an operation in the middle of the ladder and the snake, for example:

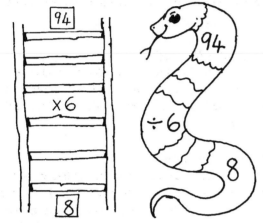

Ask the children to fill them in.

Suggestion(s) for support

Make sure the children have an understanding of the relationships between division and multiplication, and addition and subtraction. It may be more suitable for some children to work using addition and subtraction only. This will involve them in 'building up' to a number and 'taking away' from a number. Fill in the starter and target numbers for them, if necessary.

Assessment opportunities

Observe the children as they complete the activity. Are they able to use all four operations confidently? Identify those children who are hesitant in their ability to complete the reverse operations down the snake and who, therefore, need further experience of this type.

Display ideas

Choose some examples from the children's work. Ask the children to transfer the operations they used to blank paper copies of photocopiable sheet 137. These sheets can be mounted and displayed in the classroom.

Reference to photocopiable sheet

Photocopiable sheet 137 provides a blank ladder and snake for the children to fill in. The sheet could be made more challenging by writing in starter and target numbers for the children to fill in between.

FRACTIONS OF A NUMBER

To be able to calculate a simple fraction of an amount using a calculator.

†† *Pairs.*

🕐 *30 minutes.*

Previous skills/knowledge needed

The children need to have grasped the idea of a unit or whole being divided into a number of equal parts. They should be able to calculate fractions of a small group or collection, for example, $\frac{1}{2}$ of 10 or $\frac{1}{3}$ of 15. They should be confident with multiplication and division facts up to 10.

Key background information

Children who have had lots of practical experience dealing with fractions, splitting groups or sets of objects into equal parts, will come to realise that a fraction such as $\frac{1}{4}$ can be interpreted as one whole or unit divided into four equal parts. This will enable them to calculate a fraction of an amount using a calculator; for example, $\frac{1}{4}$ of 60. The unit in this case is 60. So 60 has to be divided into four equal parts. Using the calculator, they will find that $60 \div 4 = 15$, so $\frac{1}{4}$ of 60 is 15. This activity provides simple practice in calculating fractional parts of numbers. It is important that the children have had relevant practical experience beforehand.

Preparation

Make copies of photocopiable sheet 138 directly on to card or mount them. For the extension activity, use the blank 100 square on photocopiable sheet 120 to make a similar game using fractions such as $\frac{2}{7}$ or $\frac{6}{15}$.

			The 100 sq
Name _____			

1	2	3	4	5	6
$\frac{2}{5}$/20	19	$\frac{1}{6}$/18	17	16	1
21	22	23	24	$\frac{3}{5}$/25	

You may wish to make copies of this extension sheet in advance also.

Prepare the children by providing them with activities which involve them in finding fractional parts of small amounts, such as dividing, say, a set of 20 counters into quarters.

Resources needed

For each pair of children you will need: a copy of photocopiable sheet 138, two different-coloured counters, a dice, a calculator, pencils, paper, copies of the game board for the extension activity.

What to do

Give each pair of children a copy of the 100 square on photocopiable sheet 138. They will also need a calculator, a dice, a different coloured counter each, and paper and pencils with which to record their scores.

Explain the rules of the game. Each player, in turn, throws the dice and moves his counter along the 100 square that number of spaces. If a player lands on a square with a fraction on too, he must calculate that fraction of the number on that square. If he is correct, he scores the answer to the sum in points. Play continues in this way until both players have reached the end of the 100 square. The player with the most points is the winner.

Now show the children an example: If I throw a 6 on my first go and move my counter six places, I land on a square showing $\frac{1}{2}$ and 6. I now have to calculate $\frac{1}{2}$ of 6. This will give me three points because $\frac{1}{2}$ of 6 is 3. On my next go I throw a 4. Now I will move to square 10 which also shows the fraction $\frac{1}{5}$. If I calculate $\frac{1}{5}$ of 10 correctly I will earn another two points because $\frac{1}{5}$ of 10 is 2.

Before the children start to play the game, ensure that they can recognise the number squares which have fractions written on them. As they play the game, encourage them to estimate the answers. They can use a calculator to check. If necessary, remind the children about using a calculator to find a fraction of a number.

Suggestion(s) for extension

You may wish to discuss with them that finding, say, $\frac{2}{5}$ of a number is the same as finding $\frac{1}{5} + \frac{1}{5}$. So, $\frac{2}{5}$ of 50 would be 20, as 10 + 10 would be 20. Let them play the game again using the preprepared extension game board, as described in 'Preparation', where the fractions have been changed to include $\frac{3}{5}$, $\frac{5}{8}$, $\frac{3}{12}$ and so on.

Suggestion(s) for support

Spend more time with the children doing practical activities which will reinforce the ideas mentioned above. Let the children use cubes or counters, or they could use a 0–100 number line.

Assessment opportunities

Note the children's ability to calculate the fractional parts of numbers in their heads. Can they work out $\frac{1}{2}$ of a number quickly? Note how they check their answers with the calculator. Do they choose the correct operation keys? Have they grasped the notion of a fraction being an equal part of a whole?

Identify those children who need more practical experience dividing sets of objects into halves, quarters, thirds and so on.

Reference to photocopiable sheets

Photocopiable sheet 138 provides the 100 square game board to be used for the game in this activity, where a proportion of the numbers have fractions added beside them. Sheet 120 may be used to make an extension game.

SALE!

To be able to calculate a simple percentage of an amount using a calculator.

†† *Small group.*

🕑 *30–40 minutes.*

Previous skills/knowledge needed

The children should have had experience of converting fractions to percentages.

Key background information

This activity will involve the children in calculating the percentage of a number and then subtracting this from the price of items in a sale. This means they have to carry out two calculations.

For example: 20% off a garment costing £10

20% of £10 = £2

£10 – £2 = £8

Different calculators vary in the order in which the buttons should be pressed when making calculations of this sort. You will need to check the correct combination for your particular classroom calculators prior to the lesson.

Preparation

Make a copy of photocopiable sheet 139 for each child.

Resources needed

A copy of photocopiable worksheet 139 for each child, pencils, calculators.

What to do

Remind the children of previous work they have done on percentages. Ask them to identify the mathematical symbol for 'per cent' and ask them if they can remember what 'per cent' means. Explain that '10 per cent' means 'ten out of a hundred'.

Ask the group if they know any examples of situations when they might hear the phrase 'per cent'? Draw their attention to items they might see on news programmes on television or read in the newspapers which mention statistics. Other examples of percentages being used could include mortgage rates, pay increases, exam results and, finally, reduced prices in the shops at sale time.

Show the children photocopiable worksheet 139. Tell them that all the items shown are on offer in a summer sale and that the shop has reduced all the prices by 50%. Ask them to work out the sale price of each item and fill in the blank labels. Discuss with the group what 50% means. From previous work on fractions and percentages they should know that '50% off' is the same as 'half price'. So, they have to calculate half of the original price. When they have completed all the 'sale price' labels, ask them to work out what the prices of the items would be if they had only been reduced by 10%, and then if they had been reduced by 25%. They can fill in these new prices on the table given on the worksheet. As the children fill in the photocopiable sheet, ask them questions such as: What fraction is 10% equivalent to? What about 25%? What do you notice about the prices reduced by 50% and 25%?

Check that they know how to use a calculator to work out the new sale prices. If necessary show them an example: For the shoes, originally priced £30, press:

③ ⓪ ⊖ ⑤ ⓪ ⊘ ▭ 15

to find out that the shoes now cost £15 in the sale.

Suggestion(s) for extension

Ask the children to look through a clothes catalogue and choose five items. They could try using items with prices such as £9.99. They should note the prices of the items and then calculate the sale prices of each if they were reduced by 10%, 25% and 50%.

Suggestion(s) for support

Work closely with the children, encouraging them to work systematically, and recording each stage of their calculation. Limit the sale price they have to find to 50%. Delete the additional table before copying and handing out the photocopiable sheet.

Assessment opportunities

Note the children's ability to use the calculator to find percentages of prices. Do they use the calculator confidently? Do they check that the answer is reasonable, having used the skills of estimation and approximation?

Ask the children to explain to you how they have calculated the new sale prices. Use their completed sheets as evidence of their ability to calculate simple percentages of amounts, but especially use their responses to your questions and your own assessment of their confidence and ability in handling the activity.

Opportunities for IT

The children might like to explore the way in which their calculators handle percentages:

▲ can the calculator automatically add or subtract the

percentage change from the original price?

▲ how would they calculate percentages if there was no percentage key?

▲ how can they use decimal fractions to work out percentages directly (an increase of 15% can be entered as price × 1.15).

Encourage the children to see how a calculator could be used in a practical situation, and the need for estimating answers and accurate keying.

Display ideas

Ask the children to look through catalogues, magazines, newspapers and so on for examples of articles reduced in price for a sale. Collect and display these alongside questions asking the children to work out the sale prices.

Reference to photocopiable sheet

Photocopiable worksheet 139 provides the children with examples of items of clothing and asks them to work out the reduced sale prices at 50%, 10% and 25% off.

DECIMAL COVER-UP

To be able to add and subtract with decimals to two decimal places.

†† *Pairs.*

🕐 *30–45 minutes.*

Previous skills/knowledge needed

The children should be familiar with using decimal notation including tenths and hundredths. They should know how to add and subtract whole numbers.

Key background information

This activity involves children in the addition and subtraction of decimals. The decimal numbers they will be dealing with

include those equivalent to ¼, ½ and ¾. These are fractional amounts with which they are likely to be familiar.

Preparation

For each pair of children, copy photocopiable sheet 140 directly on to card or mount it securely. Cut out the 'Decimal cover-up' grid game board and cover it with clear adhesive plastic or laminate it. Also, cut out the decimal cards.

Resources needed

For each pair of children you will need: a 'Decimal cover-up' grid game board, a set of decimal cards, at least 15 counters of one colour for each player, a calculator (optional).

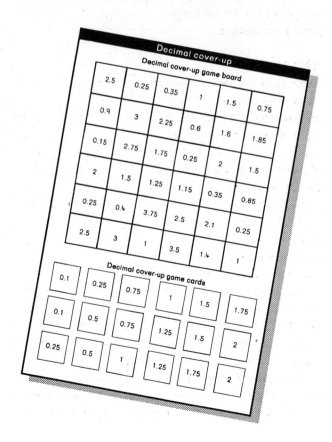

What to do

Give each pair of children a set of decimal cards, a grid game board, a calculator (optional), and at least 15 counters of one colour each.

Explain the rules of the game: The aim is to cover as many of the grid squares as possible with counters. The cards are shuffled and placed face down on the table. In turn, each player takes two cards from the top of the pack. Using either an addition or subtraction and the numbers on the cards, the player tries to make a number on the grid. If she is successful, that player puts one of her counters over that number so that it cannot be used again. After each go the cards are put on one side until the pile has been used. Then they are reshuffled and put back, face down, on the table, to be reused.

At this point, give the children an example. Show them two cards, say 0.5 and 1.25 and ask them what new numbers you could make with them. Demonstrate that the numbers on the cards could be added together to make 1.75, or, if they subtract the smaller number, 0.5, from the larger number, 1.25, they can make 0.75.

Tell the children that the player has to decide which of the operations she is going to use for the turn. Encourage the children to estimate their answers. Once they have decided which operation to use, addition or subtraction, they should use the calculator to check the answer.

Suggestion(s) for extension

After the children have played the game using addition and subtraction, they could play a version using three operations. Make two sets of 0.1–0.9 decimal cards for each pair and give them a grid like the one shown below:

0.9	1.1	0.16	0.2
0.7	1.2	1.5	0.72
0.4	0.13	0.81	0.6
0.63	1	0.12	1.3
0.14	1.7	0.36	0.5

Use the same rules, but this time allow the players to multiply the numbers on the cards, as well as add or subtract.

Suggestion(s) for support

The game board could be made shorter by making the winner the first player to cover four numbers on the board.

Alternatively, an easier version of the game could be made. From the original set of cards take out the two marked 0.1 and make a new, smaller, 'Decimal cover-up' grid, as shown below:

2	1.75	0.5	1
3.5	1.25	2	0.75
2.75	1	1.5	2.5
0.25	0.5	2.25	3.75

Assessment opportunities

Observe the children playing the game. Note whether they are able to use their skills of estimation to help them to decide which operation to carry out. Do they work out the addition or subtraction in their heads, or do they rely solely on the calculator? Can the children tell you which cards they will need to cover a particular number? From this decide whether they can confidently and accurately add and subtract decimal numbers.

Reference to photocopiable sheets

Photocopiable sheet 140 provides the grid game board and decimal number cards needed to play the game.

TARGET 10

To be able to add and subtract decimals to two decimal places.

🕐 *Pairs.*

†† *30–40 minutes.*

Previous skills/knowledge needed

The children should have an understanding of the place value of decimal fractions.

Key background information

The children will have been dealing with decimal fractions in many practical situations, such as measuring and calculating with money. This activity provides the children with practice in adding and subtracting decimal fractions in a game situation. It also gives them the opportunity to use skills of estimation and approximation.

Preparation

Make a copy of photocopiable sheet 141 for each pair of children directly or mount the copies on to card. If possible, laminate them or cover them with clear adhesive plastic.

Resources needed

For each pair of children you will need: a 'Target 10' game board, one red and one blue water-based felt-tipped pen, a calculator.

What to do

Give each pair of children a copy of the game board and a calculator. Each player uses a different coloured felt-tipped pen, for example one red and one blue.

Explain the rules of the game. The aim is to reach the centre of the circle. The first player chooses any number from the outer ring of the circle and enters it into the calculator display; for example, 0.15. (At this point, get the children to follow the example with you and enter 0.15 into their calculators.) To make a first step the player must move to one of the adjoining numbers on the second ring of the circle. He cannot jump. With this example he can move either to 1.37 or 1.29. (Point to these numbers on the game board. Make sure the children understand that once they have chosen a number they cannot jump across numbers.)

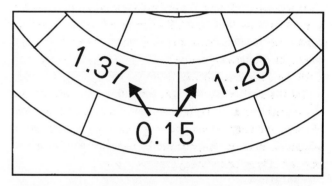

If the player decides to move to 1.37 he must tell his partner. Then he has to change the number in the calculator display into 1.37 by performing either *one or two* additions. He must not overshoot 1.37. If he gets it right he can mark the move by drawing a line from 0.15 to 1.37. If not, he loses his turn. If he reaches 1.37 in one or two additions, the next player takes a turn. The display on the calculator is cleared and Player 2 chooses a different starting number from the outer ring. Player 1 will begin again from 1.37. The first player to reach the 10 in the centre of the circle is the winner.

Ask the children for some examples of additions they could make to reach 1.37 from 0.15. They can try a few on their calculators. For example: + 1 then + 0.22; or + 0.85 then + 0.37. Encourage the children to use strategies such as rounding to the nearest whole number first.

The board can be wiped clear after each game.

Suggestion(s) for extension

Change the game so that both players begin from the centre of the circle, starting with 10 in the calculator display. The winner is the first player to get off the circle.

Suggestion(s) for support

Some children will need to work with decimals to one place first. Focus on 0.5. When the children are able to construct an addition chain to 10 using whole numbers and 0.5, introduce 0.25; for example, 1.5 + 3.0 + 3.5 + 2.0, progressing to 1.25 + 3.00 + 3.25 + 2.5.

Assessment opportunities

Observe the children playing the game. Question them about the strategies they are using to get from one decimal fraction to another. If they are constantly 'overshooting' they may need more experience with tenths and hundredths and the ways in which they can be written using the place value system.

Reference to photocopiable sheet

Photocopiable page 141 is the game board for playing the 'Target 10' game.

GUESS THE NUMBER

To be able to use mathematical reasoning and knowledge to find an answer.

†† *Individuals.*

🕐 *30–40 minutes.*

Previous skills/knowledge needed

The children need to have an understanding of all four operations. They should know some of the properties of numbers such as odds and evens, multiples and factors.

Preparation

If necessary, revise some of the properties of numbers (see above) with the children.

Make a copy of photocopiable worksheet 142 for each child.

Resources needed

A copy of photocopiable sheet 142 for each child, A4 card, paper, pencils, pens, calculators (optional).

What to do

Give each child a copy of photocopiable sheet 142. Then tell the children that from each set of clues they have to discover a 'missing' number. Ask them to read the examples on the sheet. If necessary, find the first missing number with them.

As the children work through the sheet, point out the types of clues that are used; for example, 'less than' and 'more than', specific properties of the missing number, and the clues using the four operations.

When they have completed all four questions tell the children that now they are going to make their own 'Guess the number' activity. Make sure that they plan this carefully. A number must be chosen and a set of clues organised which make finding the number possible, but not immediately obvious. Initially brainstorm together a range of clues which the children could use. Encourage them to use a variety of clue types and to use any knowledge they have about the properties of numbers. Ask them to write the clues out. You will need to check their work carefully, ensuring that it is possible to find *one* number from the set of clues.

Once this has been done, the clues can be written out neatly on to card. A collection of 'Guess the number' puzzle cards can be made for the children in the class to swap and try to answer.

Suggestion(s) for extension

Encourage the children to find out about square and cube numbers, and prime numbers. This information can then be used to make more complex clues.

Suggestion(s) for support

Go through one of the 'Guess the number' questions on the sheet. Encourage the children to think carefully about each statement. Read them through together. Then get the children to work systematically through the set of clues, crossing out the numbers they know are incorrect.

When doing their own puzzle, start the children off by giving them a missing number to work on. Choose numbers such as 50, 100 or 25 which have several fairly obvious properties from which to choose.

Assessment opportunities

The children's answers to the questions on photocopiable worksheet 142 will provide some evidence of how well they can use mathematical reasoning and knowledge of numbers to find unknown numbers.

The clues the children devise for their own 'Guess the number' activity will give you a fair idea of their knowledge and use of the properties of numbers. The clues will vary depending on the age and ability level of the children.

Watch out for the careful and logical thinking that the writing of the clues requires. Are any of the clues ambiguous or too broad to be of use? Have the children thought about the numbers used in the set from which the correct number is chosen?

Opportunities for IT
The children could use a word processor or graphics or DTP package to present their 'guess the number' examples which could be published as a class book entitled *Guess the number: our own puzzles*. They could experiment with different fonts, text sizes and formats to present an interesting layout for their work. The solution to be puzzles could be given on the last page or the children could make a small answer book.

Display ideas
Use examples of the children's work to make a puzzle book (see 'Opportunities for IT').

Reference to photocopiable sheet
Photocopiable worksheet 142 provides the children with four sets of clues which will lead them to find four numbers. The four numbers required are: **1.** 45; **2.** 116; **3.** 13; **4.** 28.

STAMPS

To be able to solve simple problems using addition.
†† *Small group.*
🕐 *30–45 minutes.*

Previous skills/knowledge needed
The children should be able to add two-digit numbers.

Key background information
This activity involves the children in combining numbers to make different totals. Using 5p and 7p stamps the children will find that they can make various amounts which they can record using a 100 square. They will reach a point when five consecutive numbers have been shaded:

$$24 \ (5 + 5 + 7 + 7)$$
$$25 \ (5 + 5 + 5 + 5 + 5)$$
$$26 \ (5 + 7 + 7 + 7)$$
$$27 \ (5 + 5 + 5 + 5 + 7)$$
$$28 \ (7 + 7 + 7 + 7)$$

All numbers can now be made by simply continuing to add 5 to each of these combinations.

Preparation
If necessary, complete and copy the 100 square on photocopiable sheet 120 for each child.

Resources needed
Completed 100 square for each child (photocopiable sheet 120), coloured pencils, paper, calculators (optional).

What to do
Tell the group of children you are working with that there is a problem you would like them to solve. The local post office has only got 5p and 7p stamps left to sell. Using only those stamps, how many different values can be made? For example, 10p can be made by using two 5p stamps and 12p can be made using a 5p and a 7p stamp.

Give the children a copy of the 100 square each. Ask them to find as many amounts as they can and to shade in the numbers on the 100 square. Encourage the children to record the combinations of 5p and 7p they used to make each different amount. Discuss with them the different combinations they can have. Ask them questions such as: How far do you have to continue making different amounts before you know you can make all the following numbers? Can you explain why?

When the children have reached 28 on the 100 square they will have shaded five consecutive numbers. Let them continue finding ways of making 29 and 30 before stopping them and asking them if they need to continue. Ask the children what can be added to 24 to make 29, and what can be added to 25 to make 30? To 26 to make 31? Encourage them to discover that they could stop working at 28 as all other numbers can be made by adding 5.

Calculations

Suggestion(s) for extension

Ask the children to carry out the same activity using 3p and 8p stamps. They could also try for 6p and 8p. Ask them to explain what happens this time.

Suggestion(s) for support

Work closely with individual children. Help them to find a systematic way of recording the combinations they find. Encourage them to use a number line; this may help them to see the point at which it is no longer necessary to keep combining 5s and 7s.

Assessment opportunities

Note how individual children record their work. Are they systematic in their approach? Were they able to recognise the point at which they could stop combining numbers? Note if they were able to use the process of addition to solve the problem.

Reference to photocopiable sheet

A blank 100 square can be found on photocopiable sheet 120.

ATTENDANCES

To be able to calculate percentage parts of quantities.

†† *Group of four to six children.*

🕐 *30–40 minutes.*

Previous skills/knowledge needed

The children will need to have a good understanding of percentages and should be able to convert fractions to percentages confidently using a calculator (see 'Fraction of 100' on page 25 and 'Percentage patterns' on page 26 in Chapter 1). Also, they need to be able to round a decimal fraction to two decimal places, and understand that this can be expressed as a hundredth; for example, 0.789 becomes 0.79 or $\frac{79}{100}$.

Key background information

This activity can be used as a follow-up to the work covered in Chapter 1 on percentages.

Resources needed

Pencils, paper, calculators.

What to do

Begin by explaining to the group that they are going to look at how many children attend school every day. They will do this for a week. At the end of the week they will display the information and explain their findings to the rest of the class.

At this point, ask the group if they have any ideas as to how this information can be presented. For example, simple statements for each day: 'On Monday 24 children were at school.' A bar chart or line graph could be used indicating the number of attendances. Discuss the ideas they suggest, considering the advantages and disadvantages of each idea. For example, does the method of display make it clear how many children there are in the class altogether? Does it tell you how many children were absent? Would you be able to use the information to make comparisons with other classes in the school?

Introduce the idea of using percentages. Remind the children of any previous work done on percentages (such as 'Fraction of 100' on page 25 and 'Percentage patterns' on page 26 in Chapter 1). Discuss the advantages of using percentages. Stress that information is more easily conveyed and that comparisons with other classes will be possible.

Help the children to work through the following example: if there are 29 children in a class and today three of them are absent. What percentage of the class are in school?

The children will need to express the number of children in school as a fraction, that is $\frac{26}{29}$. This is then changed into hundredths – a decimal. Using the calculator this works out as 0.8965517. This can be rounded to two decimal places to become 0.90. Remind the children that this can be written as $\frac{90}{100}$, and that as a percentage this is 90%. So, 90% of the children were in school. If necessary, let the children work through further examples.

Then ask them to calculate the percentage of children in

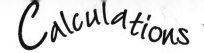

their own class who have come to school today. This information should be recorded and the same calculation carried out for each day of the week.

Suggestion(s) for extension

Broaden the activity to include finding out other statistics about the class, for example: What percentage of the class had toast for breakfast? What percentage of the class got out of bed after 8am?

Suggestion(s) for support

Spend more time explaining how to convert fractions to percentages. Use simple exercises such as ten children are in school out of a class of 20. Make sure they understand the place value of decimal notation and can round numbers to the nearest hundredth.

Assessment opportunities

Do the children understand decimal place value? Do they recognise that percentages are fractions of 100? Through discussion, determine whether they appreciate the value of presenting their information in terms of a percentage. Are the children able to carry out the necessary calculations confidently and interpret the answers correctly?

Opportunities for IT

Once the children have mastered the skill of turning data into percentages they could go on to collect information across a range of classes and use a spreadsheet to record the data, calculate the percentages and display them in graphical form.

If attendance figures were collected the spreadsheet might look like this:

	A	B	C	D	E
1		CLASS	NOR	PRESENT	%
2		Class 1	30	24	C1/D1×100
3		Class 2	32	31	C2/D2/100
4					

If the children have had more experience, they can learn how to replicate the formula which automatically takes account of the different cell references or the data in each class. Your spreadsheet may also have a direct function for working out the percentages.

Most spreadsheets now have graphical facilities which would enable the children to produce different forms of graphs from the raw or percentage data.

Display ideas

Display the percentage of attendance for each day in a prominent place in the classroom. Ask the children to write an explanation of their work to be displayed alongside the attendance record.

DOUBLE THE QUANTITY

To be able to choose the appropriate mathematical operation to solve a problem. To be able to increase a recipe in proportion.

†† *Small group.*

⏰ *30–45 minutes.*

Previous skills/knowledge needed

The children should be able to use all four operations confidently. They should have had some experience of measuring using standard weights of 1kg, ½kg, 100g, 20g and 10g. They should be conversant with metric measures.

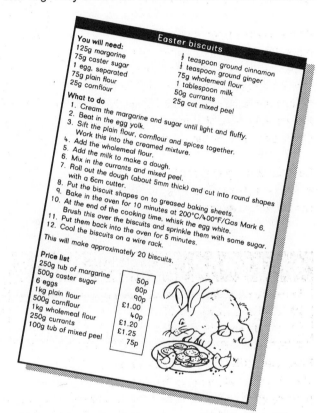

Key background information

Increasing the amounts given in a list of ingredients will involve the operations of addition and multiplication. The extension activity involves subtraction and division.

Preparation

Copy the recipe (photocopiable sheet 143) for each child. Delete the prices from the bottom of the sheet if you think they might be confusing or if you do not intend to go on to the activity 'The cost of a biscuit' on page 68.

Resources needed

A recipe sheet for each child, pencils, paper, calculators, number lines (optional).

What to do

Show the children the recipe for Easter biscuits on

photocopiable sheet 143. Give them each a copy and read through the list of ingredients together. You could read with them also the method for baking the biscuits.

Draw the children's attention to the fact that the recipe provides for approximately 20 biscuits. Ask them what you could do if you wanted to make 40 biscuits. Do they know how they could make sure that there would be enough biscuit mixture to make 40 biscuits?

Let the children discuss the problem together. Ask them to write a new list of ingredients giving the amounts they would need to make 40 biscuits. Allow them to use any equipment or apparatus they feel is necessary to work out this problem.

Follow up this activity by making the biscuits to sell to raise money for a favourite charity.

Suggestion(s) for extension
Ask the children to write a list of ingredients which will make 10 biscuits and/or 30 biscuits. Find other examples of recipes for them to adapt likewise.

Suggestion(s) for support
Ensure that the children have experience dealing with gram weights and can use decimal notation to record weights of over 1kg.

Start the children off by giving them some simple examples of recipes for one person; for example, to make one toasted cheese sandwich they will need:

2 slices of bread

1 slice of cheese

1 tomato

Ask them to work out what they will need to make two toasted cheese sandwiches.

Assesment opportunities
Look at the revised list of ingredients for 40 biscuits. Have the children successfully increased the amounts? Were they able to tackle the problem confidently, applying the appropriate operations? Use their work as evidence of their ability to carry out the correct mathematical operations to solve the problem.

Display ideas
Enlarge the photocopiable giving the original list of ingredients and mount it to card. Do the same with the children's second list. Display these alongside examples of the children's work.

Reference to photocopiable sheet
Photocopiable sheet 143 provides the recipe and amounts of ingredients which are to be increased/decreased in proportion during this activity, as well as the information on prices of ingredients for the next activity, 'The cost of a biscuit'.

THE COST OF A BISCUIT

To be able to use a calculator to solve a problem. To know which operation to apply in solving a practical money problem. To be able to calculate the cost of a single item using the concept of proportion.

†† *A small group of four to six children.*

🕐 *30–40 minutes.*

Previous skills/knowledge needed
The children should have considerable experience in using all four operations and should be able to record money both in hundreds of pence and in decimals of one pound. Work on metric measurement in weight should have been completed. It will be necessary for the children to interpret calculator displays and round numbers to two decimal places.

Preparation
Make copies of photocopiable sheet 143 (if not made for the previous activity) for each child.

Resources needed
A copy of photocopiable sheet 143 for each child, pencils, writing materials, calculators.

What to do
Distribute copies of the recipe for Easter biscuits with the price list for the ingredients (photocopiable sheet 143). If appropriate, refer to the children's experience of doing the previous activity 'Double the quantity'.

Then explain to the children that, on the basis of the recipe and the information given in the price list on the photocopiable sheet, they have to calculate:

▲ the total cost of making the biscuits;

▲ the cost of making one biscuit.

Read through the recipe with the children. Draw their attention to the list of ingredients and ask them how much margarine is needed for the recipe. Invite them to use the price list to find out the cost of margarine: 50p for 250g. Since they need only 125g, ask them to think of a way of calculating how much this will cost. One suggestion might be: 125 is half of 250, so the cost will be half of 50p which is 25p. Discuss this strategy and help the children to agree with the result.

Another suggestion might be: If you find the cost of 1g you can find the cost of 125g. This can be done on the calculator as follows:

0.50 ÷ 250 = 0.002

0.002 × 125 = 0.25.

So the cost of 125g of margarine is £0.25 or 25p.

Remind the children of money notation. To avoid confusion ask them to use the conventional decimal notation; for example, the amount 50p (£0.50) should be keyed in as 0.50 (rather than 50).

Ensure that everyone understands how to find the cost. Ask them to work out the cost of the second ingredient on their own. Emphasise the importance of estimating what the cost might be first before doing calculations on the calculator. Check the work of each child and assist individuals if necessary.

As a group, discuss the strategies different children used. Agree that the cost of 75g of caster sugar is £0.09 or 9p.

Next encourage the children to work in pairs and continue costing each of the remaining ingredients. Tell them to agree on a 'small amount' to cover the costs of the spices and milk. Allow enough time for the pairs to cost all the ingredients. Then ask them to calculate the total cost. Discuss the results and how they did their calculations. Discuss the reasonableness of the total cost and discuss the variation in the total cost due to the amount added for the spices and milk.

Finally, ask them to consider how to find the cost of making one biscuit. What operation would they use? Why? Discuss their suggestions and help them to find the cost, if necessary. Discuss any variation in the answers and try to explain it.

Suggestion(s) for extension
Challenge the children to find the cost of making 40, 60 or 100 biscuits.

Suggestion(s) for support
Let the children work collaboratively in groups of say, four, so each child could calculate the cost of two ingredients, thus reducing the amount of calculations to be done. Work with them through each stage of the calculations. Spend time approximating the answers. Use one form of money notation, modifying the photocopiable sheet if you wish to all pence (£1.25 to 125p, for example) or all pounds/ decimals (50p to £0.50).

Assessment opportunities
Note the strategies that the children use in tackling this problem. Did they know which operation to apply? Did they interpret the display on the calculator correctly? Check their completed costings.

Reference to photocopiable sheet
Photocopiable sheet 143 provides a recipe and a corresponding price list for the ingredients for it.

The costs for the items needed are:	
125g margarine	£0.25
75g caster sugar	£0.09
1 egg	£0.15
75g flour	£0.08
25g cornflour	£0.02
75g wholemeal flour	£0.09
50g currants	£0.25
25g mixed peel	£0.19
Total cost	**£1.12** (excludes the cost of spices and milk)
Total cost of one biscuit	**£0.06** (approx.)

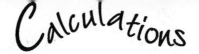

SHOPPING FOR THE KITCHEN

To be able to combine prices up to £100.

†† *Small group.*

🕐 *30–40 minutes.*

Previous skills/knowledge needed

The children should know and be able to use the notation for recording prices to two decimal places. They will need to know how the calculator displays money; for example, £5.10 is shown as:

> 5.1

They should be able to add three- and four-digit numbers.

Key background information

This activity uses the example of buying items to promote the concept of using addition in a familiar context, and provide an opportunity for the children to use their skills of estimation and approximation.

Preparation

Make (or let the children make for themselves) a stimulus sheet for each pair. Cut out appropriate pictures from catalogues or magazines, stick them on to plain paper and write the names and prices of the equipment alongside (as shown opposite):

Resources needed

A stimulus sheet showing kitchen equipment per child or pair in the group, pencils, paper, calculators, gardening catalogue (for extension activity).

What to do

Give the group the stimulus sheets. Start by discussing the various items shown and their prices. Discuss which item is the most expensive and which is the cheapest.

Tell each child to imagine that they can spend up to £100 on equipment for a school cookery room. Explain that they must choose items from the sheet. Then allow them time to select a few items and use addition to calculate the total cost of their choices. Let them use pencil-and-paper methods, or a calculator if they wish. Then ask the children in the group to compare their lists of choices. Has anyone chosen four items? If so, what is their total cost? How much change would you receive from £100? Has anyone chosen a different set of items?

Encourage the children to explain how they can calculate the change from £100. Tell them to explore all the possible combinations of items they could buy for under £100.

Suggestion(s) for extension

This activity can be extended by using, say, a gardening catalogue and asking the children to choose equipment and plants to make a small herb garden in the school grounds.

Suggestion(s) for support

Work closely with the children and ask them to choose just two items for the school cookery room. Ask them to explore the possible combinations and calculate the prices involved.

Assessment opportunities

As the children work through the activity note how they organise their work. Can they use pencil-and-paper methods to add up three or more amounts? How confidently are they able to calculate the change due from £100? Keep a record of their work as evidence of their ability to combine prices up to £100.

Opportunities for IT

A spreadsheet could be set up which shows the prices of individual items, multiplies them by the number purchased and keeps a running total of the funds remaining. The effect of any adjustment to the purchases could then be identified immediately.

Display ideas

Ask the children to draw large versions of the kitchen utensils shown on the stimulus sheets and use these as the centre of a display of the children's maths work.

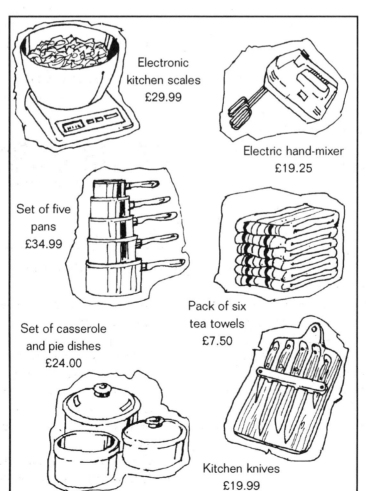

Electronic kitchen scales £29.99

Electric hand-mixer £19.25

Set of five pans £34.99

Set of casserole and pie dishes £24.00

Pack of six tea towels £7.50

Kitchen knives £19.99

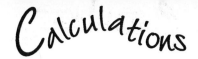

THE SCHOOL TRIP

To be able to solve problems involving addition of amounts of money.

†† *Individuals.*

🕐 *30–40 minutes.*

Previous skills/knowledge needed

The children should be able to deal confidently with decimals to two decimal places.

Key background information

This activity will involve the children in calculating the cost of a class trip. They are given two alternative destinations and details of the charges of two coach companies. Using this information the children have to find the most cost effective trip for the class.

They will need to add up the cost of four alternatives:

▲ a trip to the art gallery using coach company A;

▲ the same trip using coach company B;

▲ a trip to the museum and castle using coach company A;

▲ the same trip using coach company B.

The cheapest trip would be to the museum and castle using coach company A.

If you are planning a school trip at some time this activity would be all the more valuable using real data relating to local attractions. Let the children research and then price the trip, following the format of the activity described below.

Preparation

The information needed for this activity could be written up on the board or flipchart for the children to copy, or be presented on a sheet which you have written out and copied for each of them. They will need to know that:

▲ There are 32 children going on the trip.

▲ Art gallery: entrance fee – none; pupil worksheets – 10p each; the gallery is approximately 30km from school.

▲ Museum and castle: entrance fee – 50p each; pupil worksheets – 5p each; the museum and castle are approximately 19km from school.

▲ Coach company A charges £2 per km, plus 50p per passenger.

▲ Coach company B charges £3 per km, with no extra charges.

Resources needed

Board or flipchart, marker pens, paper, pencils, calculators.

What to do

Read through the information from the board or stimulus sheet with the children, and explain that they have to find out the cost of each trip using company A and company B, in order to decide which is the cheapest alternative. Establish with the children what it is they have to find out in order to discover the cheapest trip. Stress that they will need to work systematically, working through the possible alternatives. Ask the children to record the cost of each possibility.

Suggestion(s) for extension

Ask the children to calculate how much each alternative trip would cost *per child*. Encourage them to use skills of approximation – they will need to round numbers to the nearest penny.

Suggestion(s) for support

Help the children to organise their work. Through discussion, help them to see that there are four possibilities they need to consider.

Assessment opportunities

Note how the children tackle the problem. Do they use the appropriate operations? Are their calculations accurate? Do they use pencil-and-paper methods or rely solely on the calculator? Through questioning, try to determine how well they use skills of estimation and approximation.

MISSING NUMBER

To be able to estimate and approximate solutions to division problems.

†† *Pairs.*

🕐 *30–40 minutes.*

Previous skills/knowledge needed

The children should understand the process of multiplication and division and be able to deal with two- and three-digit numbers confidently.

Key background information

This activity involves children in estimating the approximate size of a missing number in multiplication and division sentences. This ability is a necessary skill in order to use a calculator effectively and to check whether an 'answer' is reasonable.

Rounding numbers to the nearest 10 is a useful strategy in approximating answers and the children need to have a good grasp of place value principles.

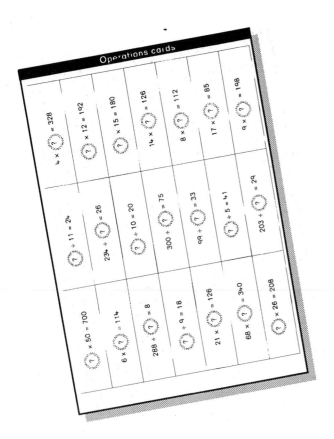

Operations cards

Preparation

For each pair of children, copy photocopiable sheet 144 directly or mount the copies on to card. If possible, laminate them or cover them with clear adhesive plastic. Then cut the sheets into individual operations cards.

Resources needed

For each pair of children you will need: a set of operations cards, a calculator, paper, a pencil.

What to do

Give each pair of children a calculator, a pencil and some paper for scoring, and a set of operations cards. Tell them to shuffle the cards and place them face down on the table. Each player, in turn must pick a card and try to guess the missing number. They can try out their guesses using the calculator. For each attempt the player makes he scores one point. The winner is the player with the *lowest* score when all the cards have been used.

Provide the children with an example:

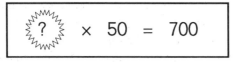

$$? \times 50 = 700$$

Tell them that the player who picks this card might try keying into the calculator: $20 \times 50 = 1000$. This is too big. Her next attempt might be $13 \times 50 = 650$. This is too low. The player may now see that another 50 is needed, so $14 \times 50 = 700$. As the correct number was found in three attempts the player would score three points.

As the children play the game, encourage them to use skills of estimation and approximation. Before they make their guess using the calculator, ask them questions such as:
▲ Is the missing number more or less than 10?
▲ How can you tell?
▲ What if you round the answer on the card to the nearest 10. Does this help you?

Remind them of rules they may know about multiplication and division. For example, an even number multiplied by another even number always gives an even product, and any number multiplied by 5 gives an answer ending in 0 or 5.

Take the opportunity to remind the children that division is the inverse of multiplication. If they know that $10 \times 20 = 200$, then they can see that the missing number on the card: '$? \div 10 = 20$' is 200.

As the children work through the cards get them to keep a record of their scores. The lowest total score wins.

Suggestion(s) for extension

Adapt the activity to include larger numbers. The children could try to make their own set of operations cards.

Suggestion(s) for support

The activity can easily be adapted so that the children are working with smaller, more manageable numbers. Make a set of simpler support cards using multiplication and division sentences. For example:

$3 \times ? = 36$	$45 \div ? = 15$
$? \times 6 = 36$	$? \div 10 = 10$
$4 \times ? = 12$	$49 \div ? = 7$
$? \times 3 = 33$	$? \div 5 = 20$
$8 \times ? = 56$	$90 \div ? = 9$
$? \times 4 = 48$	$? \div 6 = 6$
$2 \times ? = 52$	$32 \div ? = 4$
$? \times 7 = 63$	$? \div 8 = 7$
$5 \times ? = 20$	$21 \div ? = 7$
$? \times 9 = 45$	$? \div 4 = 20$
$6 \times ? = 42$	$50 \div ? = 5$
$? \times 8 = 40$	$? \div 2 = 35$

Alternatively, provide the children with a selection of numbers from which to select the answers to the operations cards.

Assessment opportunities

Observe the children as they play the game. How many attempts are they making before finding the correct number?

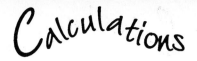

Are they able to estimate sensibly or are they making wild guesses?

Note how they progress through the game and whether they improve as they gain more experience.

Reference to photocopiable sheets
Photocopiable sheet 144 provides a set of operation cards needed for the game.

FIND THE RULE

To be able to check results using inverse operations.

Individuals.

30 minutes.

Previous skills/knowledge needed
The children should be able to use the four operations.

Key background information
The first part of this activity involves the children in discovering how two numbers have been used to generate a new number; for example, 6 and 2 are multiplied together to produce 12.

The second part of the activity involves discussion with the children on how they can use the numbers to check their answers. They should be aware that subtraction is the inverse operation of addition and that $X = a - b$ means $X + b = a$. Also, that division is the inverse operation of multiplication and that $X = a \div b$ means $X \times b = a$.

Preparation
Make a copy of photocopiable worksheet 145 for each child.

Resources needed
A copy of photocopiable worksheet 145 for each child, paper, pencils.

What to do
Give each child a copy of photocopiable worksheet 145. Look at the first table together. Here, the rules have been given and the children only have to do the calculations. Help them to work systematically. Encourage them to study the first row of numbers carefully and to work on one rule at a time. They should check that the rule applies to all the examples given.

If the children complete this first table confidently, read through the explanation for the second part of the activity together. Emphasise to the children that this time they have to discover the rule for each column, so there are five rules to find altogether. Start the children off by asking questions such as:

▲ What has been done with the two numbers in the first row, 6 and 4, to get the number in column A, 2?

▲ Are there any other numbers in column A filled in? (Explain that the same rule will apply to them.)

As the children discover the rules, ask them to make sure they work for all the examples that are filled in for that column already.

When all five rules have been discovered and the numbers in all the columns filled in, ask the children to explain, in written form, each rule.

Next, discuss with them how they can use the numbers to check that the answers are correct. For example, ask them to look at column B. The rule was to multiply the two numbers together: $6 \times 4 = 24$, $9 \times 3 = 27$, $10 \times 4 = 40$, $4 \times 2 = 8$, and so on.

They can use the same numbers to check their answer by using division: $24 \div 4 = 6$, $27 \div 3 = 9$, $40 \div 4 = 4$, $8 \div 4 = 2$, and so on.

Ask the children how they could check the answers in column C. If necessary, point out that although the rule involved division, they can use multiplication as a check: $10 \div 2 = 5$, so $5 \times 2 = 10$; $12 \div 2 = 6$, so $6 \times 2 = 12$; $14 \div 2 = 7$, so $7 \times 2 = 14$, and so on.

Discuss with the children their ideas for checking the rules for the remaining columns.

Suggestion(s) for extension
The children will enjoy the challenge of working on their own 'Find the rule' activity sheet for others in the class to complete.

Name _____   Date _____

The first two numbers in each row have been used to make new numbers. Follow the rules given below to fill in the rest of the table.

Numbers	A Add the two numbers together.	B Subtract the second number from the first number.	C Multiply the two numbers together.	D Multiply first number by 2 and add on the second.
3 and 2		5		
7 and 3		1		
6 and 1		4	6	
4 and 3	7			8
9 and 4				13
5 and 5			36	
8 and 2		0		
10 and 5	15			18

Find the rules (A to E) and fill in the rest of the table. Each letter represents a different rule.

Numbers	A	B	C	D	E
6 and 4	2	24	5		
9 and 3	6			20	100
10 and 4			6		
4 and 2		40			
8 and 6					140
18 and 2	2			12	
6 and 2			7		
14 and 10		12		16	200

Suggestion(s) for support

Delete the second table before copying and distributing the sheet, so that the children only have to 'follow', and not 'find', the rules.

Assessment opportunities

The completed sheet(s) can be used as evidence of the children's ability to identify successfully the five rules used to generate the numbers on the chart. Concentrate on one or two children. Spend time discussing with them the ways in which they can check their answers. Note if they have grasped the idea that division is the inverse of multiplication and that they can use this fact to check their answers.

Opportunities for IT

The children might like to extend this activity on to a spreadsheet to give them experience of writing formulas and referencing cells.

Reference to photocopiable sheet

Photocopiable worksheet 145 provides two charts for the children to complete by following and then finding the rules being applied to sets of given pairs of numbers.

The five rules being used in the second chart are:

▲ A – subtract the smaller number from the larger number, for example, $8 - 6 = 2$;

▲ B – multiply the two numbers, for example, $6 \times 2 = 12$;

▲ C – add the two numbers and divide by 2, for example, $(9 + 3) \div 2 = 6$;

▲ D – add the two numbers and multiply by 2, for example, $(4 + 2) \times 2 = 12$;

▲ E – add the two numbers and multiply by 10, for example, $(18 + 2) \times 10 = 200$.

HOUSE NUMBERS

To be able to check addition through adding a set of data in a different order.

†† *Large group or whole class.*

🕐 *20–30 minutes.*

Previous skills/knowledge needed

The children should be able to add two- and three-digit numbers.

Resources needed

Paper and pencils (optional).

What to do

You can choose any list of random numbers as the basis for this task. For example, ask the children in the group/class to tell you the number of the house or flat in which they live.

As they report the information, record it so they can all see the list.

House/Flat number
7
4
10
134
61
3
17
5 … .

Now ask the children to add up the list of numbers. There may be as many as 30 numbers. When this has been done, ask them to consider a way of checking that the information is correct. Encourage them to add the column of numbers from the opposite direction. Discuss the different ways in which the children found the total. Stress that they can check their result by adding the numbers in a different order. The order of addition makes no difference to the answer.

Suggestion(s) for extension

A smaller group of children could generate their own data to add up. Examples might include their heights in centimetres or their dates of birth. Another good real-life source of numbers would be to use supermarket till receipts. Collect these yourself and from colleagues and photocopy them for the children to use. Ask them to check their work by adding in a different order.

Suggestion(s) for support

Work with those children who need extra support. Arrange to have a smaller group, say four or five children. This facilitates dealing with a smaller volume of information. They will only have four or five numbers to add up. Go through the same procedure as above: the children should add the column of figures from the top down and from the bottom up. Discuss how this is a good way to check the accuracy of the result.

Assessment opportunities

Observe the children as they work. Do they check their addition by adding in a different order? Can they add the numbers mentally? Note their knowledge of number bonds and their confidence in applying them.

CHECK YOUR ROUTE

To be able to check addition through the use of subtraction.

†† *Pairs.*

🕐 *30 minutes.*

Previous skills/knowledge needed

The children should understand the process of addition and subtraction.

Preparation

Copy photocopiable sheet 146 directly on to card for each child. If possible, laminate or cover the copies with clear adhesive plastic.

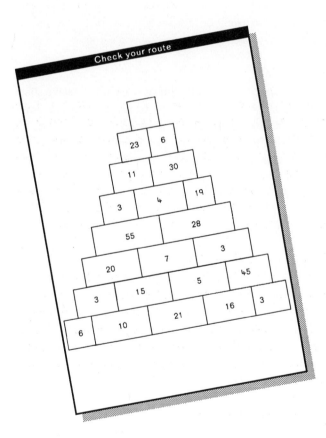

What to do

Give each child a copy of photocopiable sheet xxx. Explain that they must each choose a route from the bottom to the top of the pyramid and mark this on the sheet using a coloured pencil or felt-tipped pen. They should then add together the numbers along the route and write the total at the top of the pyramid.

For example:

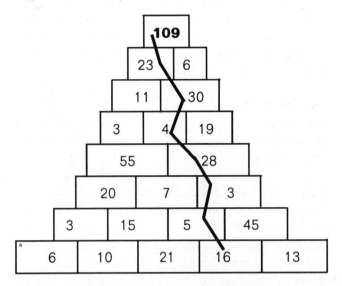

$16 + 5 + 3 + 28 + 4 + 30 + 23 = 109$

The totals are checked by the second child in each pair who begins with this top number and works backwards down the route subtracting the numbers.

For example: $109 - 23 - 30 - 4 - 28 - 3 - 5 - 16 = 0$

Discuss with the children the advantage of checking addition by using subtraction. Each child should try at least five routes on the pyramid. If the sheets have been laminated, the totals can be wiped clear at the end of each turn. Otherwise, the children can use a different coloured pencil for each route to avoid confusion.

Allow the children to use calculators to check the addition routes through subtraction.

Resources needed

A copy of photocopiable sheet 146 for each child, coloured pencils or water-based felt-tipped pens (for laminated sheets), calculators (optional).

Suggestion(s) for extension

Adapt the pyramid to include larger numbers.

For example:

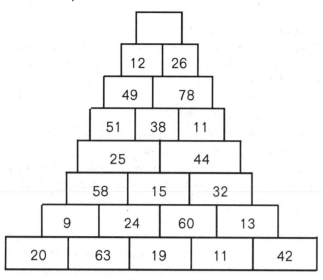

Suggestion(s) for support

Work with those children who need extra support. Make a copy of the pyramid and adapt it to use smaller numbers. Let the children use calculators to check their work.

For example:

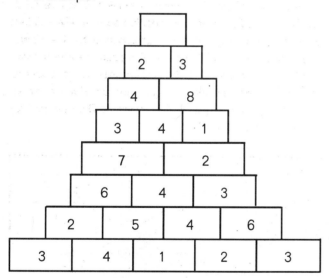

Assessment opportunities

Observe the children as they work. Decide whether they are able to check addition using subtraction. Note their knowledge of number bonds and their confidence in applying them.

Reference to photocopiable sheet

Photocopiable sheet 146 offers a selection of numbers in the form of a pyramid for the children to add. This sheet can be adapted to use larger or smaller numbers for extension or support work respectively.

THE SAME TOTAL

To be able to cross-check by adding numbers in a different order.

†† *Individuals (or pairs).*

🕐 *30–40 minutes.*

Previous skills/knowledge needed

The children should be able to add numbers confidently. They should have had experience of completing magic squares.

Key background information

The following activity provides children with practice of addition facts to 20 as well as giving you the opportunity to stress the importance of cross-checking by adding numbers in a different order.

The first part of the activity involves completing addition squares and adding the totals of the columns and rows to cross-check that it has been filled in accurately.

The second part of the activity involves placing digits in a particular order on grids so that the numbers along the lines have the same total. The activity is designed to be completed by individual children. However, pairs of children could work together, particularly on the second part of the activity. In this way they would check each other's work.

Preparation

Make a copy of the blank 100 square on photocopiable sheet 120 and amend it into an addition square (as shown below). Copy this addition square and photocopiable sheet 147 for each child. Photocopiable sheet 122 provides some magic square puzzles and can be used for support. (The corresponding 'Square magic' activity is given on page 31 of Chapter 2.) You may like to copy this sheet in advance too.

+	1	2	3	4	5	6	7	8	9	10
1										
2										
3										
4										
5										
6										
7										
8										
9										
10										

Resources needed

For each child you will need: an addition square, a copy of photocopiable sheet 176, a pencil and writing materials, a calculator (for support).

$\mathcal{C}$alculations

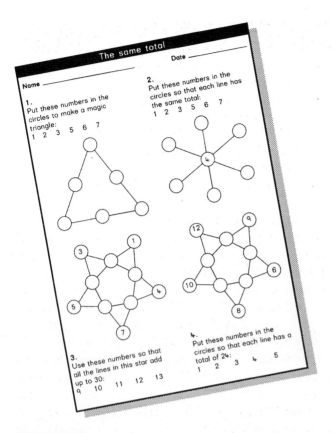

The same total

Name _____

Date _____

1. Put these numbers in the circles to make a magic triangle:
1 2 3 5 6 7

2. Put these numbers in the circles so that each line has the same total:
1 2 3 5 6 7

3. Use these numbers so that all the lines in this star add up to 30:
9 10 11 12 13

4. Put these numbers in the circles so that each line has a total of 24:
1 2 3 4 5

What to do

Begin by reminding the children how to fill in an addition square and distribute the blank addition squares. Ask the children to complete them as quickly as possible. This should be a straightforward activity for the children with a high rate of success.

When the addition squares have been filled in, ask the children to add up all the numbers in the first row. Then ask them to add up all the numbers in the first column. What do they notice?

Let them check that the total of the second row is the same as the second column, the third row the same as the third column and so on. They should then check the totals with those of the child sitting next to them.

Now introduce the second part of the activity. Remind the children of work they have completed on magic squares and discuss with them why they are known as 'magic squares'. Distribute copies of photocopiable sheet 147. Tell the children that all the puzzles on the sheet are 'magic'; that is, numbers are put in the circles so that the totals of numbers along the lines are the same. Ask them to work through the four puzzles on the page. For the second two the magic number is provided. The children will need to check their attempts by adding the numbers along each line, cross checking with other lines in the puzzle.

Suggestion(s) for extension

Find examples of similar puzzles for the children to work on; for example, magic squares, magic triangles, arithmagons and so on.

Suggestion(s) for support

Give the children similar, but more simple, puzzles to work on. Photocopiable sheet 122 provides examples of 'magic square' puzzles to start them off.

Assessment opportunities

Use the completed addition square as evidence of children's knowledge of addition facts to 10 + 10.

Observe the children as they work. Note whether they systematically cross-check their work by adding numbers in different orders.

Display ideas

The children could draw the number puzzles on to a large card. This could form part of a display which includes work on magic squares. The children could also research how magic squares were used by earlier civilisations.

Prepare some puzzle cards for the children to work on and put these beside the display.

Reference to photocopiable sheets

Photocopiable sheet 120 provides a blank 100 square which can be adapted easily into an addition square. The children are required to complete all the addition facts to 10 + 10 and check their work by finding the total of each row and column.

Photocopiable sheet 122 can be used for support to remind the children about magic squares. Photocopiable sheet 147 provides four number puzzles. The solutions to the puzzles are:

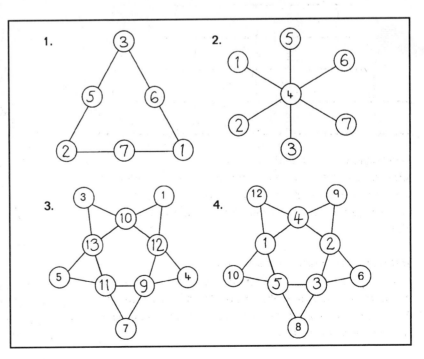

HIDDEN NUMBER

To be able to check calculations by using inverse operations.

†† *Pairs.*

🕐 *30–40 minutes.*

Previous skills/knowledge needed

The children should be able to use the four operations confidently. They should know that division is the inverse operation of multiplication.

Resources needed

Calculator for each pair, paper, pencils.

What to do

Explain to the children how to play this game.

The first player in each pair chooses a number which the second player has to discover. Player 1 enters her chosen number into the calculator and performs four operations.

For example: 12 is entered into the display.

$$\times 2$$
$$+ 6$$
$$\div 10$$
$$- 1 =$$

2 is shown on the display.

Player 1 writes down on paper the operations and the finishing number *only*. Player 2 is given the list of operations and now has to use the inverse operations to discover the first player's hidden number.

For example: 2 is entered into the display.

$$+ 1$$
$$\times 10$$
$$- 6$$
$$\div 2 =$$

12 is shown on the display.

A point is scored by Player 2 if the number is discovered. If not, Player 1 scores a point. Each player has four turns. The winner is the player with the most points.

As the children play the game, emphasise that they are checking that the calculations performed on the hidden number are correct by using the inverse operation and 'undoing' the operations.

Suggestion(s) for extension

Suggest that the children perform six or more operations on their secret number.

Suggestion(s) for support

Start the activity by restricting the operations to addition and subtraction. For example, Player 1 could start with 15 and enter + 20 – 6. Player 2, starting with 29, would carry out the check by entering + 6 – 20.

Assessment opportunities

Observe the children as they play the game. Note their ability to apply inverse operations to reach the hidden number. Use the children's record of the operations they have used to discover the hidden number as evidence of their understanding of how to use inverse operations.

Handling data

The authors of *Mathematics in the National Curriculum* (DfE, January 1995) acknowledge that the sections of the programme of study interrelate. For example, it is stated that calculating skills should be developed in number and through work on measures and handling data. It is highly desirable, therefore, that activities designed to develop concepts of handling data and probability should be included in a book concerning the teaching of number. An understanding of number is necessary for and developed through data handling and probability activities.

This chapter is divided into two sections concerning handling data (pages 80–88) and probability (pages 89–94). Since data handling should have purpose and be in response to a genuine question, the activities in this chapter are presented in the context of a theme (Our class), rather than as separate tasks, and cover questioning, collecting information, analysing and recording the recorded information.

Probability is about judging uncertainty. These activities aim to help the children to understand probability through experiment, as well as introducing appropriate language and the probability scale.

SETTING UP A DATABASE

To be able to set up and explore a database on the computer. To search for and find information on a computer database. To be able to list information from a computer database. To be able to sort information on a computer database. To be able to do a print-out of information.

†† *Whole class, then groups of two or three children.*

🕐 *This activity might continue over a week rather than being completed in one lesson.*

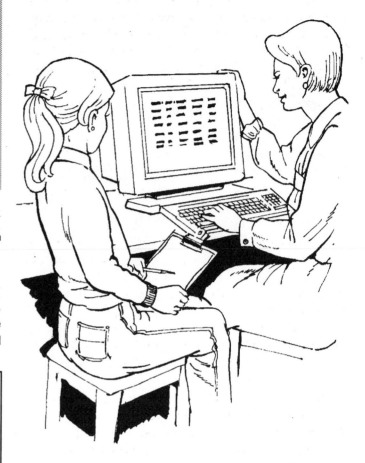

Previous skills/knowledge needed

The children should be able to use the keyboard on a computer.

Key background information

Before the advent of computers, the information collected, for example through the questionnaire on photocopiable sheet 148, would probably have been transferred to record cards as follows:

Name	ATKIN, Jane
Girl	Yes
Brothers	3
Sisters	0
Age	7
Birthday	June

Name	BAILEY, Rob
Girl	No
Brothers	1
Sisters	2
Age	7
Birthday	March

Computers allow the user to sort this information in different ways with greater speed, accuracy and efficiency – they are far more flexible than traditional record cards.

A database is a collection or 'base' of data. Depending upon the age and ability of the children this could be done by the teacher in advance so that the database is ready to use, or the teacher could set up the structure of the database and then the children can enter their own information ready for later use by the class. If a database is set up well on the computer, it can be used to answer a range of questions.

The usefulness of a database is often decided by the way data is organised under headings or 'field names'. When all the information relating to one item/person is entered this is known as a 'record'. For younger children it is sensible to keep the number of different headings (field names) small so that they are not overwhelmed by the amount of data.

Consider the types of questions that you are likely to ask before deciding. A mixture of numerical data and textual data is useful, particularly for later use in drawing graphs. You may not want to put in children's surnames unless you have several children with the same forename. Adding the sex of the child provides a useful starting point for discussions about

how computers cannot tell the difference between boys and girls just from the names.

If children are adding their own data they are likely to need support, both to ensure that they know how to enter and edit their data and that they enter it correctly. This activity could be used to improve children's general IT skills, such as the use of the keyboard, cursor keys and mouse. An extra adult in the form of ancillary help or a parent can be useful here. Try to start work well in advance of actually needing to use the data as it may take several days to get every child to enter their data. You may also want to check the database through before you start to use it, as extra spaces, full stops and so on can affect the later use of the database. Make sure you save more than one version of the database so that if children alter or amend things you have another copy to use.

Preparation

Before embarking on this task, a variety of information about the children needs to be collected. Photocopiable sheet 148 offers a questionnaire which can be used to do this. Each child should complete the questionnaire, perhaps as a follow-up to discussion about the topic and/or as a reading/writing activity. You may wish to provide different or more information, depending on the interests of the particular children. In the case of some of the questions, say, favourite pop group, football team and TV programme, you might also arrange for the children to collect responses from children in one or more other classes. (This data can be used later for comparative purposes and in drawing up scaled charts.) The completed sheets should be collected from each child and checked for completion and accuracy.

Arrange for groups of two or three children to work at the computer.

Resources needed

Completed questionnaire (see Preparation), computer(s) with suitable software package, printer and computer paper.

What to do

Begin by asking the children to think of a way of structuring the data they have collected about the class members on the computer. Ask them to consider, say, the first four questions on the questionnaire and how they can record the information.

It is important at this stage to give the children the opportunity to explore and find out from their own mistakes. Allow time to discuss in pairs and to devise a basic database. Ask more focused questions such as:

▲ How could we record the information so each member of the group could print out the information themselves?
▲ How could we record the information so we can list all the names of the people who completed the questionnaire?
▲ How could we record the information so we can identify or make a list of all the boys in the class?

Our class

1. What is your name? ___
2. Are you a boy? [ ] Yes [ ] No
3. How many sisters have you got? ___
4. How many brothers have you got? ___
5. ▲ I am [ ] cm tall.
   ▲ My handspan is [ ] cm.
   ▲ My foot is [ ] cm long.
6. What age are you? ___
7. In what month is your birthday? ___
8. List the pets you have ___
9. Do you have a bicycle? [ ] Yes [ ] No
10. Do you play chess? [ ] Yes [ ] No
11. What is your favourite hobby? ___
12. What is your favourite TV programme? ___
13. Name the best book you read this year: ___
14. Do you play a musical instrument? [ ] Yes [ ] No
15. If so, what is it? ___
16. What subject do you like best in school? ___
17. How do you travel to school? [ ] Walk [ ] Car
    Bus [ ] Taxi
18. What is your favourite pop group? ___
19. What is your favourite sport? ___
20. If you have a favourite football team, state it: ___

Through discussion of the above questions, you may decide together on the following field names: NAME, GIRL, BROTHERS and SISTERS. Encourage the children to take it in turns to key in at least some of his or her own record.

Help each of them to extract and print their own record. Then challenge them to produce a list of all the children who play chess or who have a bicycle or have a birthday in the same month as themselves. This will involve teaching them how to use the 'search', 'print' and 'list' options.

Finally, draw children's attention to the three sources of information:
▲ the questionnaire;
▲ the database on the computer screen;
▲ the print-out of the database.

Focus on one piece of information from the database, for example the names of the people in the class. Encourage the children to examine the three sources of information for this aspect and check their results. Also draw their attention to the efficiency of the technology over manual recording in providing the information.

Suggestion(s) for extension

Encourage the children to ask questions of the data which would involve further searching. For example, identify the people who play a musical instrument and determine how many of this group *also* play chess.

Suggestion(s) for support

Children needing extra support should be given further opportunities:
▲ to discuss the best way to record the information;
▲ to be helped to appreciate the need for field names;
▲ to find out how to key in, access and print out their own records.

Time should be spent with these children in a one-to-one setting helping them to interpret their own record from the print-out. This should be done with reference to the three sources of information: questionnaire, database on screen, and print-out.

Assessment opportunities

Note individual children's responses to the questions you ask, and their suggestions regarding how to record information providing evidence of their understanding.

Are they able to interpret their own and others' records appropriately and confidently? Identify children who may need extra experience doing these activities.

Can they access their own records? Can they use the 'search' option and the 'sort' option to extract information? Can they do a print-out of that information?

Reference to photocopiable sheet

Photocopiable sheet 148 provides a questionnaire on which to base this activity.

BAR GRAPHS

To be able to present data in a bar graph. To recognise that the same information can be presented in different ways. To be able to interpret data presented in a bar graph. To be able to compare bar graphs showing the same data from different groups.

†† *Large group or whole class.*

🕐 *30–40 minutes.*

Previous skills/knowledge needed

The children should have had lots of experience of sorting information and recording it in different ways; for example, presenting and interpreting data on pictograms and on block graphs.

Key background information

A graph is a 'picture' illustrating some information or 'data'. Pictograms represent data through the use of individual pictures for each item of data. Although they provide an attractive means of presenting information, their disadvantage is that they may not allow you present information precisely.

A block graph presents information in a series of blocks such that each block represents one or more item(s) or person(s). If you are using a scale of one to one (1:1) each block represents one item or one person as in the following example:

Favourite drinks of children in the class

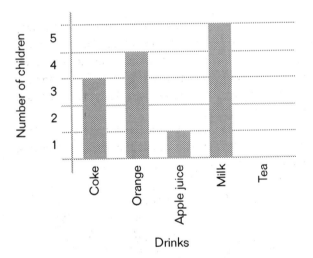

Each occurrence is shown as a separate unit on a block graph, and each block should be the same size. The number of occurrences is written in the spaces between the lines on the vertical axis.

In bar graphs, information is presented as a series of bars. The number of items in each category is shown by the height of the bar. In the following example a bar graph is used to present the same information as in the above block graph.

Favourite drinks of children in the class

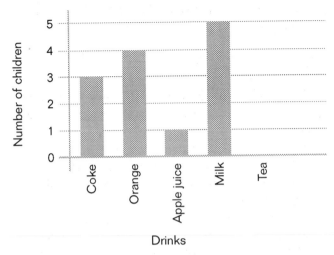

The bar graph differs from a block graph in the following ways: the height of the bar denotes the number in that category and, therefore, zero should be presented on the (vertical) axis. The numbers on the vertical axis should be placed *on* the lines, rather than in the spaces (between the lines), to ease interpretation.

A few basic rules should be followed in the drawing of all graphs:

▲ Give the graph a title.

▲ Space the categories evenly so that all the blocks/bars are the same size/width.

▲ Label both the horizontal and vertical axes.

▲ Label each separate category or bar on the horizontal axis.

Whether to use a block or a bar graph is a matter of preference when presenting discrete data. Discrete data increase in 'jumps'. For instance, if the data relate to the numbers of children in families then the figures recorded will be 0, 1, 2, 3 and so on. $1\frac{1}{2}$ children is impossible. If fractions of a unit are not possible, the data will increase in jumps from 0 to 1, 1 to 2 and so on. If the variable in question is discrete (for example, favourite pop group) then it is appropriate to leave gaps between the bars. This helps to emphasise the 'separateness' of each category. If, however, the variable in question is continuous (for example, the length of hand spans) then it is appropriate not to have gaps or spaces. Adjacent bars should touch each other to indicate that the horizontal axis is a number scale.

It is better to familiarise children with block graphs before introducing them to bar graphs.

Preparation

Collect information involving a large amount of data, for example, the favourite pop groups, football teams and TV programmes of the children in two classes. This information should be tallied and a tally table produced by the children beforehand.

Alternatively, the accessing of the database and the tallying could be done as part of the lesson.

Resources needed

Large sheets of card, board or flipchart, markers, paper, writing materials.

What to do

Explain that the purpose of this task is to document the data on the favourite pop groups of the children in the class and to go on to compare their choices with those of the children in the next class.

Refer to any previous work done on block graphs and possibly displayed in the classroom. Refer to the characteristics of block graphs and the conventions of graph drawing such as a title, labelling the axes and making sure that the categories or blocks are evenly spaced.

Discuss the different ways that could be used to present the information about the favourite pop groups of the children in the class. Draw a block graph on the board or flipchart based on information from the tally table.

Pop groups	A	///
	B	##//
	C	### ### /
	D	//
	E	### //

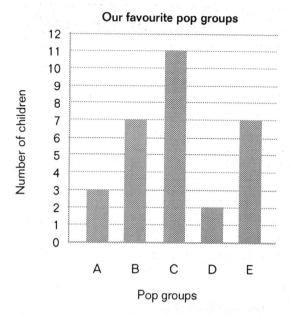

Our favourite pop groups

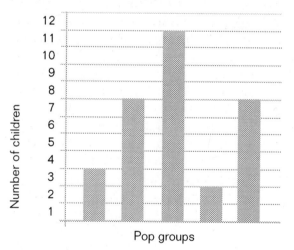

Our favourite pop groups

Encourage the children to interpret this graph and offer summary statements, for example:

▲ The same number of people chose B and E.

▲ C is the favourite pop group of most of the members of the class.

▲ 30 people took part in the survey.

Next explain that this information can be presented in another way. Demonstrate how to make a bar graph using the same information(as shown in the following diagram).

Draw attention to the fact that the same information is being presented in a different format. Refer to ways in which bar graphs are similar to and different from block graphs. Discuss the differences, the main one being that in the bar graph, they do not need to show the separate blocks to represent each separate occurrence. Clarify the conventions for presenting information as a bar graph if necessary (see 'Key background information').

Next discuss the findings of the graph using a more analytical approach. Encourage the children to reflect on whether the same information for another class might be different. What about data from older or younger children? What about information from children of their own age living in another country?

Then go on to present the data from another class (already collected and tallied) on another bar chart. Discuss this bar chart and encourage the children to make summary statements and to ask questions as before. Then compare both bar charts. What are the main similarities and differences between the two classes?

The children may then go on to construct their own bar charts based on different information, for example, favourite football teams of two classes in the school.

Suggestion(s) for extension

Encourage those who are ready for a further challenge to present continuous data using a bar chart, for example, for the height of children in the class. They will need access to the class database. They will have to decide which variable goes on each axis: number of children and height.

Suggestion(s) for support

When introducing the idea of bar graphs use Cuisenaire rods or colour factor rods to show the length of the bars. This helps to reinforce the concept of a bar chart.

Assessment opportunities

Note individual children's responses to the questions you ask. Can they make summary statements about the bar graphs? Are they able to make comparative statements about the two classes? Identify children who may need extra experience doing these activities.

Display ideas

Display the completed bar graphs in the classroom with the summary statements attached. However, discuss with the children that graphs are meant to be useful rather than decorative.

SCALED BAR GRAPHS

To be able to interpret data presented in a bar chart using different scales on one of the axes. To recognise that the same information can be presented in different ways, using different scales.

†† *Large group or whole class.*

🕐 *30–40 minutes.*

Previous skills/knowledge needed

The children should have had lots of experience in sorting, recording and presenting data on block and bar graphs using a scale of 1:1.

Key background information

When presenting data about large numbers of items on a graph it is essential to use a scale. The skill of reading scales

involving large numbers is important for the correct interpretation of graphs. The block graph below displays data on favourite colours using a scale of 1:2. Each block represents two people. Scaled block/bar graphs share all the characteristics of simple block/bar graphs. You can also indicate the scale if you wish, but this is not necessary.

Preparation

Collect a large amount of data, for example, the favourite pop groups, football teams and TV programmes of people in, say, two classes. This data should ideally be made into a computer database. Access the data from the database. This will be in terms of numbers of children preferring different TV programmes. You might like to present this on a tally table on the flipchart.

Resources needed

Data on favourite TV programmes of two classes of children extracted from database, marker pen, flipchart or board, paper, writing materials.

What to do

Explain that the purpose of this exercise is to document the data on favourite TV programmes of the group of children in two (or more) classes.

Revise any previous work done on block/bar graphs and refer to the characteristics of a bar graph. Discuss ways of presenting the tallied information. On the flipchart draw a 5 x 5 grid and begin to record the information. As you go on to present this information the children discover that the grid is too 'small' to accommodate it. Discuss possible solutions to this problem: Would it be a good idea to leave out the data that won't fit on this grid? Can we let each line stand for more than one person? Lead the children to agree that a scale is needed on the vertical axis to accommodate all the data. Consider what scale should be used: one space for two people or 1:2; one space for five people or 1:5, and so on.

Decide what scale should be used, say 1:2, and then on the flipchart draw axes and labels for a bar graph: about 10

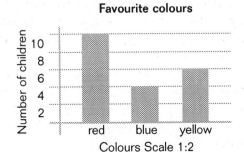

Favourite colours — Colours Scale 1:2

'units' on the vertical axis and space for about six categories on the horizontal (check the data). Add a title. Next construct the chart from the data showing one unit on the vertical axis representing two people. Demonstrate how to represent an odd number of TV programmes on a scale of 1:2, by helping them to agree the halfway point on the grid. Complete the chart. Discuss the results, ensuring that each member of the group understands the scale and can interpret the findings.

Ask questions which would require the children to interpret the scaled graph:
▲ Which is the most popular programme?
▲ Which programme did ten people like best?
▲ How many people took part in the survey?

To challenge them further ask them to consider other possible scales:
▲ What about having each square stand for three people?
▲ Would this be a good idea? Why? Why not?
▲ How would the graph change if we used a 1:4 grid?
▲ What would you have to do to make sure everyone knew how we made the graph?

Refer to the fact that numbers on one of the axes change, but that the names on the other axis remain the same.

Next get children to divide into pairs. Distribute the same information to each group, for example, the favourite hobby of people in two classes. Encourage them to present this information on a scaled bar chart. They should decide which scale to use. Encourage them to compose a brief interpretation of the graph and write it down.

Conclude the lesson by sharing and comparing the completed bar graphs and summary statements. The discussion should focus on the different scales the children used and why they chose them. They should also be reminded of the characteristics of scaled bar charts.

Suggestion(s) for extension

Encourage those who are ready for a further challenge to present the data from several classes, or from all the classes in the school, on one scaled bar graph. The children will need to decide what scale to use to handle this volume of data.

Suggestion(s) for support

These children could participate in the main activity down as far as the pair work. Then, to make the task simpler, reduce the volume of data to be processed by using only information collected in their own class. Use a scale of 1:2.

Assessment opportunities

Note the individual children's responses to the questions you ask. Do they appreciate the need for a scale? Are they able to decide what the scale should be (with your support)? Can they make and interpret the scaled bar graphs? Identify those children who may need extra experience doing these activities.

Opportunities for IT

Before starting on block or bar charts check which sort your database can draw. Some software does not discriminate between a bar graph and block graph.

Once the children have mastered the concepts involved in selecting the scale and axis they might experiment with the class database to see how the computer manages the same problem. They could compare the two outcomes and see if the same decisions were made by the computer and which bar graphs are the easiest to interpret and understand.

The children could also use simple graphing software to represent the results of a class survey or their tallying chart taken from the class computer database.

Display ideas

Display the completed scaled bar graphs in the classroom with summary statements attached. Alternatively, present them in a class book entitled, for example, 'Favourite things of children in Classes III and IV'.

LINE GRAPHS

To be able to present data on a line graph. To recognise that the same information can be presented in different ways by switching the information on the horizontal and vertical axes. To recognise that the same information can be presented in different ways using different scales.

†† *Large group or whole class.*
🕐 *30–40 minutes.*

Previous skills/knowledge needed

The children should have had lots of experience presenting and interpreting data on pictograms, on block graphs and on bar charts. They should also understand the use of a scale in presenting information.

Key background information

Line graphs are used to show how two sets of data change in relation to each other. Thus, line graphs usually concern one or two sets of 'continuous data'. Continuous data, theoretically, has an infinite number of possible sub-divisions, for example height or time. For certain continuous data, the individual values can be chosen at equal intervals and plotted as if the data were discrete (that is, could not be sub-divided, such as children or cars). This type of graph is particularly common in science and geography.

The data may be plotted as a 'bar line' graph first. A bar line graph is a development of a bar graph. Instead of 'bars', lines are used. These are then removed and instead a point indicates each value. The set of points is then joined up to form a line graph.

Sometimes this is called a 'trend graph', because it shows the trends of change in the data. For example: the diagrams below show part of a weather graph:

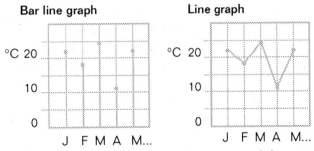

Bar line graph   **Line graph**

Line graphs are useful for comparing several data sets too – it is not necessary to draw another graph, two or more lines can be drawn on the one graph, perhaps using different colours. The children may have seen graphs in newspapers or holiday brochures showing both the maximum and minimum temperatures each month at a holiday resort.

Preparation

The data collected using the questionnaire does not lend itself to this type of representation. The need to use a line graph is most likely to arise through science investigations or when measuring the weather. Look out for opportunities discuss and practise data handling in such situations.

Resources needed

Marker pen, flipchart or board, paper, writing materials.

What to do

The topic 'Our class' may include experiments, such as the time taken for the pulse rate to return to normal after exercise, or investigations into the classroom environment, such as how the class temperature varies over the day compared to that outside.

In either of these examples, the children would make measurements at regular time intervals. Put their data on the board or flipchart and discuss how this infromation could be converted into a graph.

Explain that you are going to introduce a new type of graph – a line graph – to enable the children to interpret information presented in a variety of ways and to give them choices regarding presentation. Discuss what this graph might look like, given its name. You may like to explain about its other name – a 'trend' graph. Talk about being 'trendy'. The children should be able to relate this to being fashoinable or popular, and thus see that a trend graph shows which values in the data are the most 'popular'. Help the children to decide which axis to use for each variable. Time, for example, is usually displayed on the x axis. They should also decide if a scale is needed and, if so, of what size and on which axis.

On the flipchart, draw appropriate axes and labels for the line graph (check the data) and add a title. Construct the graph as a bar line graph. Lead the children to see that this graph is much the same as a bar graph, but instead of 'bars' there are lines, which often indicate a measure of something rather than a frequency. Then complete the graph by removing the lines and joining the points to make a line graph.

Discuss the results, ensuring that each member of the group understands the scale. Help the children to interpret the graph by questioning them appropriately. For example, if they measured their pulse every minute, can they read off the value of their pulse after two and a half minutes? If they measured the temperature every hour from 9 am, what was the temperature at, say, 10.30 am? Ensure that they understand that a line graph assumes that there are values which could be measured in between those given.

Next ask them to consider whether the same information could be presented by putting it on the opposite axes. Discuss the implications this has for the scale. Ask the children to do this, working in pairs. Share the results.

Suggestion(s) for extension

In order to develop the children's data handling skills move on to collecting and representing true continuous data rather than discrete measurements. The 'Our class' questionnaire includes a number of questions that will generate this sort of data; for example, height or handspans. It is necessary to 'group' this data and devise a frequency chart.

For example:

Height (cm)	Height	Frequency
120	100–110	0
119	111–120	//
126	121–130 ...	// ...
128 ...		

This data can then be presented as, for example, a block or bar chart. Handling continuous data is a skill only required of the most-able children.

Suggestion(s) for support

Provide the data to be plotted; for example: one pencil costs 10p, two pencils cost 20p and four pencils cost 40p. Work together to plot the data on a large sheet of paper. Help the children to see that they can work out any intervening costs from the gaph – three pencils will cost 30p, for example.

Assessment opportunities

Note individual children's responses to your questions. Can they make and interpret a line graph? Do they appreciate what sort of data could be presented in this way? Are they able to select appropriate scales?

Opportunities for IT

The children might like to experiment to see how the computer manages this activity. They could compare the computer print-out with their own graphs. Which graphs are the easiest to interpret and understand? They could also use simple graphing software to represent the data.

Display ideas

Display the completed line graph(s) in the classroom with summary statements attached.

MEAN AND RANGE

To understand, calculate and use the mean of a set of data. To understand, calculate and use the range of a set of data.

†† *Whole class or large group, then pairs.*

🕑 *30 minutes.*

Previous skills/knowledge needed

The children need to be able to use the four operations of number: addition, subtraction, multiplication and division.

Key background information

It is useful to be able to summarise a set of figures or a data set in some way. There are two frequently-used summary statistics – the *mean* and the *range*. The first offers a number as representative of the data set, while the second gives an indication of how varied or spread out the numbers in a data set are.

The *mean* summarises a collection of numbers. To calculate the mean you sum the numbers and divide by the total number of numbers in the set. For example, the average or mean age of ten children is the sum of all their ages divided by 10. A mean is calculated when you need to get some typical or representative value for your data set.

The mean is not necessarily always the best 'typical' or most representative value. For example, if half the class got 1% in their maths test and the other half got 99%, the mean of 50% would not represent the data set at all. Here it would be inappropriate to calculate a mean – it would be better to report two 'typical' scores.

Another measure of representative value is the mode – this is the most commonly occurring value in the data set. For example the following values indicate the shoes sizes of 9 people: 2, 3, 3, 4, 4, 4, 4, 5, 5. The mode is 4.

A third method of calculating a typical or representative value in a data set is the median – this refers to the point or value in the data set above (or below) which lie 50% of all the scores/values. For example, 4 is also the median in the above example. If there is an even number in the data set, the two central values are averaged, that is, added together and divided by two.

A frequency table is used to present data when there is the possibility of an occurrence happening more than once, for example in the case of numbers of brothers and sisters in the class. If, say, three children in the class have no brothers, it would be helpful to draw up a frequency table before calculating the mean. A frequency table is not difficult for children to interpret or construct once they are familiar with tally tables.

The *range* is a measure of how 'spread out' a set of data is. The range of a set of numbers is the difference between the highest and the lowest numbers.

Preparation

Access relevant information from the database; for example, number of brothers or number of sisters of children in the class. This data could be prepared beforehand and presented on a tally table (or taken from a block, bar or line graph, if these are available).

Number of brothers

0	/
1	////
2	### //
3	###
4	/

Resources needed

Calculators, paper, writing materials.

What to do

Begin by asking the children to examine the data presented in the tally table or graph, for example the data on the number of brothers of children in the class. Pose the following programme: we want to find just one number which would represent all the information on the tally table or on the graph – one number to represent the number of brothers of children in this class. How could we go about finding a suitable number. We could call this number the average.

The children may suggest the most common number. Suppose this is 2; that is, 2 is the most frequently-occurring number in the data set. This is an excellent response.

Invite them to consider other possibilities. Introduce the idea of the mean. It is (another) average. Ask then how they would calculate the mean number of brothers for the class. Help them to do this by first drawing up a frequency table as follows:

Number of brothers	Frequency	Number of brothers × frequency
0	1	0
1	4	4
2	7	14
3	5	15
4	1	4
	18	37

In order to calculate the mean we need to calculate the total number of brothers of children in the class and divide by the number of children in the class. The total number of brothers is calculated by multiplying across the rows and adding this column. So there are 37 brothers altogether. There are 18 children in the class. Using calculators the children will conclude that the average is 2. Discuss the meaningfulness of the answer – although there is 1 left over or a remainder of 1, we don't say 2.05 people as this is meaningless. Draw attention to the fact that the mean and the mode in this case are the same.

Help the children to understand that the mean and mode do not always need to be the same. Demonstrate by 'changing' the data, identifying the mode and calculating the mean again. Ask which is the most suitable value.

Help the children to see that the mean is a very good way of calculating an average as it takes into account all the values in the data set, not just the most commonly occurring one. Therefore, it is likely to be more representative than the mode.

Go on to discus the idea of range. Sometimes it is useful to know how spread out or how varied the data set is: are all the values much the same or do the figures vary a great deal? If there is a big gap between the highest and the lowest value we conclude that the data vary a lot. If there is little or no difference the data vary very little. This gap or difference is known as 'the range'. The range for the data in the example above is 4, that is 4 – 0 = 4.

Now ask the children to work in pairs and examine the information on sisters. Again they will need a tally table. They should draw up a frequency table and then identify the mode, and calculate the mean and the range.

Suggestion(s) for extension

Challenge this group to work with a larger data set by asking them to find out the average number of brothers and sisters of children in the class.

They will have to consider whether they need to combine both data sets on brothers and sisters, and then calculate the mean, having devised a new frequency table. They should consider *beforehand* whether they could add the two means already obtained through the main activity and divide by two. Will this be the same? (It should be, of course.)

Suggestions for support

Work only on the mean in one lesson.

Assessment opportunities

Note individual children's responses to the questions you ask. Can they understand the process of calculating the mean and the range? Do they know why they would want to calculate these statistics? Their own work will provide evidence of their understanding and ability to calculate these. Identify those children who may need extra experience doing these activities.

Opportunities for IT

Older or more-able children might explore the ability of a computer database spreadsheet to provide mean and range information from a set of data.

PROBABILITY LINES

To recognise that the probability of any event lies between impossibility and certainty. To understand and use correctly some basic probability terminology: impossible, very unlikely, unlikely, likely, very likely and certain. To be able to order these terms according to the degree of probability. To be able to use a probability scale to estimate, compare and justify likelihood.

†† *Large group or whole class, then pairs, then large group or whole class again.*

⏱ *45–60 minutes.*

Previous skills/knowledge needed

This activity assumes no previous knowledge of probability, although some basic vocabulary such as *certain, impossible, perhaps* is assumed.

Key background information

There are many words which are used to describe 'chance' or 'probability'. They range from *impossible* at one extreme to *certain* on the other. In between lie *very unlikely, unlikely, likely* and *very likely*. Other language is also used, for example *almost certain, probable, possible, never* and so on. This terminology offers a qualitative description of probability or likelihood. This activity demands that the children think about these terms and apply them correctly.

Probability can also be measured quantitatively. A numerical scale can be used to describe the probabilities denoted in language, as above. For example, you can think of the range of possibilities in terms of a number line from 0 to 1, as follows:

Impossible   Likely   Certain

$$0 \text{————} \frac{1}{2} \text{————} 1$$

For example, it is impossible to live forever, it is likely to rain sometime during the month of April, and it is certain that we grow older.

This activity also encourages the children to relate the descriptive terms to the numerical descriptions.

Preparation

Make a set of probability cards each about 5 × 20cm with the words *impossible, very unlikely, unlikely, likely, very likely* and *certain* written on them. Laminate the cards or cover them with clear adhesive plastic, if possible.

Prepare a set of 20 blank cards for the children to use.

Resources needed

To work with the class you will need: a set of probability cards (one for each term of probability in the verbal scale), 15–20 blank cards, crayons or felt pens (optional), length of string to make a (probability) line in the classroom, six bulldog clips.

What to do

Begin by asking the children to make up a sentence expressing something which is *impossible*. Ask them to go on to make up sentences expressing something which is *very unlikely, likely, very likely* or *certain*. Examples might be:

▲ The day after Sunday is Monday.

▲ We are going to Mars on a school trip.

▲ We are getting younger.

▲ It will rain this afternoon.

▲ We will have chips at dinner today.

▲ Everyone in this class will be absent tomorrow.

Note all of these statements on the blank cards until you have about 15–20 examples.

Next show the children the probability cards and ask them to help you place them in order starting with *impossible* and ending with *certain*.

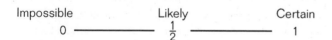

Hang them in order on the line using bulldog clips and then challenge the children to arrange their statements, with your help, in order of likelihood from *impossible* to *certain*. (You may wish to structure this part further by first asking the children to find the *impossible* statements, then the *certain* statements and then those that come in between.) Discuss their decisions and encourage the use of probability language by asking questions such as: Does everyone agree? and, Why do you think it is certain?

Encourage the children to justify their choices by referring to their own experience and knowledge. Once the class or group have agreed on the probability level for each statement the children can clip them to the relevant card on the probability line.

Next ask the children to work in pairs and distribute a set of blank cards (six) to each pair. They should write their names and the date on each card (for future reference), and then they should make up one statement about themselves for each of the six probability terms, for example one pair might decide it is *very likely* that they will watch *Neighbours* tomorrow ('We will watch *Neighbours* tomorrow'), but another pair might write that it is *unlikely* that they will watch *Neighbours* tomorrow. Each pair must decide where their own statements should be placed on the probability line. Once

NUMBER

each pair has ordered their statements, compare and share their efforts as a class or in a large group setting. As appropriate, note that the events may vary in likelihood for different people. It is important that all children justify the likelihood they attach to an event.

Finally, ask the children to consider a number scale instead of/or alongside the word scale. Write the terms on the board as a probability line and then write 0 under the first term (impossible) and 1 under the last (certain). Place $\frac{1}{2}$ in the centre of the verbal scale as follows:

impossible	very unlikely	unlikely	likely		very likely		certain
0			$\frac{1}{2}$				1

Discuss how the numbers 0 and 1 relate to the words impossible and certain and consider how the remaining terms come between these extremes. Their statements could be mapped on to the numerical scale. If the children raise the issue of $\frac{1}{3}$, $\frac{1}{4}$ and so on, they can be encouraged to place these fractions along the numerical scale and map the verbal terms according to how best they think they relate. For example, 'unlikely' and 'likely' should be placed on either side of $\frac{1}{2}$. (They may decide that thirds or sixths would be easier to map). However, at this stage it is not necessary to go beyond the two points of 0 and 1 depicting the extremes.

Suggestion(s) for extension

Ask the children to work in pairs and select a theme, possibly within the current class topic. They should then make up some probability statements in relation to the theme and place them on a numerical probability line, justifying their choices. An example might be:

impossible	very unlikely	unlikely	likely	very likely	certain
0					1
I will grow to be a giant(ess).	The children in this class will all go to bed at exactly the same time.	Someone in this class will become a member of Parliament.	We will go on a school trip this year.	We will do some writing in school today.	We would die if we did not eat or drink.

Suggestion(s) for support

If necessary, use a simpler version of the qualitative scale placing statements under three categories: *impossible, in between* and *certain*.

Assessment opportunities

Listen carefully to individual children as they describe their statements. Do they use a range of probability words and phrases to explain their decisions and ideas? Do they do

this confidently? Do they use the language associated with the extremes of the scale; that is, *impossible* and *certain* accurately? Do they use the intermediate language appropriately; that is, *very unlikely, unlikely, likely, very likely*? Can they apply the numerical scale and relate it to the verbal scale?

On the basis of the discussion and the children's statements, note any who do not yet appreciate the terminology and the means of describing relative likelihood.

PROBABILITY AND PREDICTION

To recognise and use the concept of evens and even chance. To recognise that an event has one or more possible outcomes. To list the possible outcomes of an event. To be able to predict outcomes where there are two possibilities.

†† *Large group or whole class, then pairs, then large group or whole class again.*

⏲ *30–45 minutes.*

Previous skills/knowledge needed

This activity assumes that the children have encountered some basic language of probability such as *impossible, very unlikely, unlikely, likely, very likely* and *certain* (see previous activity).

Key background information

Probability deals with events and outcomes or possibilities. The terms 'outcome' and 'possibility' are used synonymously. Each event has at least one possible outcome. For example, the event – tossing a coin – has two possible outcomes – heads or tails. There is an *even chance* of getting a head or a tail whenever a coin is tossed.

Probability can be expressed as the number of events divided by the number of possibilities:

$$\text{Probability} = \frac{\text{the number of events}}{\text{the number of possibilities}}$$

For example, when tossing a coin the probability of getting a head is $\frac{1}{2}$. This is because there is only one event – the toss of a coin – and the number of possibilities is two (a head or a tail) thus giving the fraction, $\frac{1}{2}$.

Resources needed

Coins, paper and writing materials, calculators.

What to do

Begin by asking the children what might happen if you toss a coin. Ask them what possible outcomes there could be (heads or tails)? Make sure the children appreciate that there

As the number of tosses pooled increases, the children should be able to see that there is a fairly even distribution of heads and tails. Draw their attention to this and introduce the term *even chance* or *evens* to describe the likelihood of getting a head or a tail whenever a coin is tossed.

Suggestion(s) for extension

Ask the children to work in pairs and to consider how many possible outcomes there are if they toss two coins. Remind them that there is one event and that there are two possible outcomes (head or tail) in the case of one coin. Then help them to realise that with two coins there are four possible outcomes: HH, HT, TH and TT. There is still only one event: the tossing of two coins. The probability of getting any one of the four possible outcomes is ¼ (one event divided by four possibilities). Challenge the children to list all the possibilities when tossing three/four coins.

Suggestion(s) for support

Continue the activity to an experiment involving tossing a coin 20 times, recording the result and comparing this with their predictions. Understanding will be enhanced through the experiment. The children may need to do the experiment several times to realise that there is an even chance getting heads or tails. Encourage them to share the results of their experiment using the terms 'even chance' and 'equal chance'. Can they state how many possibilities there are each time?

Assessment opportunities

Note the children's responses. How accurate are their predictions? Can they justify their predictions? Are they convinced by the evidence they collect? Are they able to interpret this evidence correctly? Do they use the language appropriately; that is, *evens, an even chance*?

Opportunities for IT

Let the children use graphing software to plot a graph of the coin tossing. They could experiment with different forms of graphs, handling pie charts and block graphs, and then discuss which displays the information in the most useful way.

Display ideas

Produce a graph of the coin tossing and display it in the classroom. A pictogram of coin rubbings, showing the appropriate numbers of heads and tails would be appropriate.

are only two possible outcomes. Ask them to think about the chances of getting either a head or a tail. What do they think would happen if they tossed the coin 20 times? Discuss their suggestions and then, with the children working in pairs, ask them to write down their predictions to the following questions:

▲ If you throw a coin 20 times, how many times will you get heads?

▲ How many times will you get tails?

Encourage the children to say why they think that they will get the results they have predicted.

Next tell the children that you want them to test their predictions by throwing a coin 20 times. They should take it in turns to throw, and record each result using a five-bar tally:

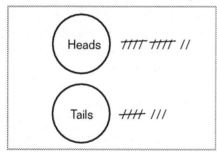

Ask the children to discuss their results with their partners and compare the actual outcomes to their predicted ones. How accurate were their predictions? Are they surprised with the actual outcomes or are they as they predicted? Next they should pool their results with another pair. How many tails resulted from 40 throws? How many heads resulted from 40 throws? Encourage them to examine the results carefully. What do they notice?

Allow the children to collate the results from two other pairs. They can use calculators to help them to total the heads and tails and the total number of tosses if they require them.

A FAIR GAME?

To be able to distinguish between fair and unfair. To be able to place events in order of likelihood. To recognise that different outcomes may result from repeating an experiment.

†† *Group of four children.*

🕐 *45–60 minutes.*

Previous skills/knowledge needed

The children need to have an understanding of and be able to use the idea of events and be able to use some of the language of probability to describe the likelihood of some events.

Key background information

A fair game is a game in which each player has an equal chance of winning.

Preparation

For each group, prepare (or help the children to prepare) two circles of card approximately 10cm in diameter. The bases do not move, each has a pointer to be spun round as the bases of two spinners. For the spinning pointers, open out two large paper clips, as shown below.

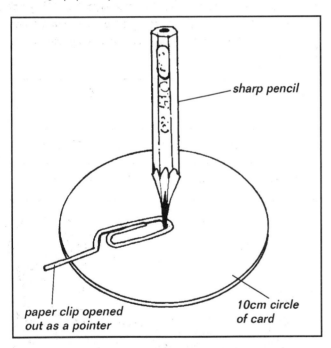

sharp pencil

paper clip opened out as a pointer

10cm circle of card

To spin the pointer, put a pen or sharp pencil in the middle of the base through the curved part of the paper clip and flick the clip to make it rotate around the point of the pencil. These can be made in the lesson, if you prefer.

Resources needed

For each group of four children you will need: two 10cm circles of card, a sharp pencil, a variety of crayons, paper clips.

What to do

Explain to the class how to construct a spinner if this has not been done beforehand. Each group of four children should have two blank spinners. They should use four different colours to colour one of the spinners in roughly the following proportions:

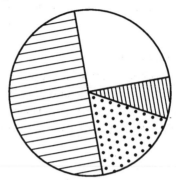

Next explain to the children that they are going to play a game. Demonstrate how to use the paper clip as a pointer on the spinner base. Position the pointer in the centre of the spinner and spin it around the pencil or pen. Tell each of the four players to choose one of the colours on the spinner. Then they should take it in turns to spin the spinner. If they spin their own colour they get one point. The first person to reach four points wins the game. Allow them to play several times.

Having played the game several times, ask the children to discuss whether they believe the game is a *fair* game. Who, if anyone, stands the best chance of winning? Why? Ask the children to explain why they believe what they think. How do they know?

Help them to come to the conclusion that a *fair* game is one in which each player has an *equal chance* of winning and that an *unfair* game is one in which players have an *unequal chance* of winning (as in this example!)

Go on to discuss whether the same person in each group won every time. Why not? Discuss that there is a chance, albeit a very slim one, that the person who is most disadvantaged by the rules of the game could still win. (Remember that in any experiment involving likelihood or chance, there is no guarantee that the different outcomes will occur in exact proportion to the [theoretical] probability of their occurrence).

Ask the children to rate the chances of each colour winning from most likely to least likely: Who is most likely to win and why? (The person with the largest coloured segment.) Who is least likely to win and why? (The person with the smallest coloured segment.) Are there any players who have an equal chance of winning? (Any whose coloured segments are the same size.) They may wish to play again to test their predictions.

Finally, ask the group to use the other blank spinner to design a suitable spinner for a fair game for four people. (Equal quarters of each colour.)

Suggestion(s) for extension

This group could design spinners so that two of four players have a good chance of winning and two have a poor chance of winning. They should play the game in order to test their predictions. Let them go on to consider different games (for example 'Snakes and ladders', 'Noughts and crosses') and to make variations to them so that these games become unfair.

Assessment opportunities

Note the reasons the children give for their predictions. Are they sensible? Do they use a range of probability words and phrases to explain their decisions and ideas? Do they do this confidently? Do they appreciate the idea of a *fair* game.

Opportunities for IT

The children could use a simple graphing program to draw pie charts of their results and compare them to the colour spinner.

DICEY GAMES

To be able to test the probability of throwing a particular number on a 1–6 dice. To recognise that the more trials of an experiment, the greater is the estimate of the outcome(s).

†† *Pairs, then group of four or six children.*

🕐 *30–45 minutes.*

Previous skills/knowledge needed

The children need to understand and use the idea of events and be able to use some of the language of probability to describe the likelihood of some events.

Key background information

This activity involves testing the assumption, held by many children, that a 6 is harder to get than any other number on a 1–6 dice. When a (fair) dice is thrown, there are six equally-likely outcomes. The probability of throwing, say, a 1 is $\frac{1}{6}$ as there is a 1 in 6 chance of throwing a 1 (or any other outcome). There is an *even chance* of throwing a 1, 2, 3, 4, 5 or 6. A general working definition of probability is the number of events divided by the number of possibilities:

Probability = $\dfrac{\text{the number of events}}{\text{the number of possibilities}}$

The chance of throwing any number on a fair dice is 1 in 6 or $\frac{1}{6}$.

This activity involves testing the likelihood of getting a 6 and comparing this likelihood to that for other numbers on the dice. The children will work in pairs and carry out some experiments, recording their results. At the end they combine the results of all the pairs to discover that the more trials that are carried out, the more even the distribution. The extension activity may raise the issue of adding probabilities. As stated, the probability of getting any number between 1 and 6 on a throw of the dice is $\frac{1}{6}$. The chance of getting, say, either a 2 or a 3 is $\frac{2}{6}$; that is, the chance of getting 2 is $\frac{1}{6}$ and the chance of getting a 3 is $\frac{1}{6}$, therefore the chance of getting either a 2 or a 3 is $\frac{1}{6} + \frac{1}{6} = \frac{2}{6}$, 2 chances in 6.

Resources needed

For each pair you will need: a dice and shaker, pencil, paper.

What to do

Begin by making the statement that: 'It is harder to get a 6 than any other number when you throw an ordinary dice.' Ask the children to say whether they agree with you or not. Can they give reasons for their views? How many times do they think they would get a 6 if they threw a dice, say, 30 times? Would they get a 6 more often than a 2, a 3 and so on? Invite them to suggest ways of testing this hypothesis or statement. They will need to think of ways of recording their results and agree on how many rolls of the dice they would have to make to be sure of testing this well (all the children should agree to use the same number – 30 is sufficient).

Ask the children to work in pairs and to devise their own recording sheet. They can use their own layout, but they will need to be able to record how many times a 1, 2 and so on were thrown. Encourage them to use a tally sheet, for example:

Number thrown	1	2	3	4	5	6
Tally	⊬⊬⊬	⊬⊬⊬	////	///	////	⊬⊬⊬ /
Frequency	5	5	4	3	4	6

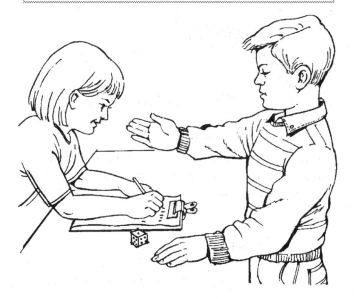

Once the children have thrown the dice 30 times and recorded the throws, ask them to examine the frequencies and discuss the results. Do they still think that it is harder to throw a 6?

In a large group session, record the total frequencies for each number of the dice obtained by all pairs, for example:

Number thrown	1	2	3	4	5	6
Pair A	4	7	3	5	7	4
Pair B	5	5	4	3	4	9
Pair C	4	6	4	8	5	3
Pair D	8	4	4	6	7	1
Pair E	5	4	8	3	4	6
Total frequency	26	26	23	25	27	23

When all the results have been collated, examine the distributions. Consider again whether it is harder to get a 6. Find the total frequency for all (say, 150) trials. The children should be able to see from the distributions that all numbers are equally likely. Draw their attention to the greater similarity of the numbers in the *total frequency* row, where there is a much more even distribution of each number rolled. Can they explain why this is so? Help the children to realise that the more frequently the experiment is carried out, the greater the chances of getting an even distribution – in this example, a frequency of 25 for each number on the dice, or 1/6 of 150.

Suggestion(s) for extension

Challenge the children to make up about four statements and four questions about probabilities and dice for example:
▲ There are six possible outcomes.
▲ You are equally likely to throw each number.
▲ The probability of getting a 5 is 1/6 or 1 out of 6.
▲ The probability of getting either a 4 or a 6 is 2/6 or 2 out of 6 (See 'Key background information,) or the probability of getting a 0 is 0/6, or 0 out of 6, or 0.

▲ What is the probability of getting a 1 or a 3?
▲ What is the probability of getting less than 6?
▲ What is the probability of getting an odd number?
▲ What is the probability of getting a number greater than 2?

Suggestion(s) for support

This activity could be used to provide further experience of assessing probabilities (it should not be used instead of the main activity). Play a game in pairs. Using a dice and some counters, let the children take it in turns to throw a dice. If the result is a 1, or a 6, then Child A can take a counter. If the result is any other number Child B can take a counter. The first person to get three counters is the winner.

Let the children play several times. How often did each player win? Is it a fair game? Discuss the reasons for the children's answers. (It is *unfair* to Child A as she has only a 2 in 6 chance of winning while Child B has a 4 in 6 chance.)

Assessment opportunities

Note the reasons the children give for their predictions. Are these sensible? Do the children use a range of probability words and phrases to explain their decisions and ideas? Do they do this confidently? Do they know how to calculate the probability of throwing a given number on a dice? Do they know how to calculate this if several games are played?

Opportunities for IT

The children could use a simple graphing program to represent their results by drawing block or pie charts.

Assessment

The National Curriculum demands that teachers' own professional judgements play a greater role than ever in informing teaching and learning. Effective assessment could be said to be at the heart of this good practice for it identifies strengths and points to means of overcoming weakness. It can provide reliable and valid information on a child's progress and can help the children themselves in taking their learning forward.

Within the activities in this book, formative assessment opportunities have been identified within the lesson plans. The activities suggested in this chapter are designed to support the teacher in summarising achievement in number at the end of the key stage, and may be used, therefore, to support the updating of teacher-assessed levels.

These short, teacher-directed activities focus on particular number objectives or, for efficiency and manageability, on a cluster of objectives. The primary aim is to assess learning, although the activities themselves also provide for learning-oriented interaction with the child, and depending on the activity, between the children. Guidance is offered on what to look for during the assessment and how to interpret the outcomes, with specific questions for you to answer in relation to each child's response to the demands of the assessment task.

From the child's point of view the modes of assessment incorporated into these summative activities include: carrying out tasks set by you using concrete materials; carrying out tasks without the aid of concrete materials; solving problems; discussing ideas; responding to instructions; and recording results/solutions to problems.

From the teacher's point of view, the styles of assessment involve: setting up particular tasks with built-in checking procedures; questioning; listening; and observation.

NUMBER STRUCTURE

To be able to create the largest and smallest three-digit number possible from three given digits. To round numbers to the nearest 10 and 100. To be able to multiply three-digit numbers by 10 and 100.

†† *Individuals.*

🕐 *30 minutes.*

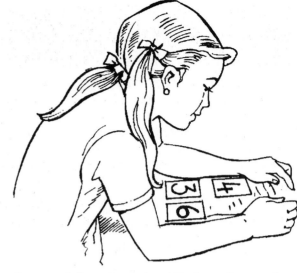

Previous skills/knowledge needed

The children should have had experience dealing with large numbers and know that the position of a digit signifies its value.

Key background information

This activity incorporates aspects of the work covered in the tasks contained in Chapter 1, 'Number structure'. For assessment purposes, you should focus on the children's individual responses to the questions on photocopiable assessment sheet 149.

Preparation

Photocopy the required number of assessment sheets. Prepare at least one set of 0–9 number cards using photocopiable page 106. Each child will need three cards in order to carry out the activity.

Resources needed

A copy of assessment sheet 149 for each child, calculators, at least one set of 0–9 cards, pencils, paper.

What to do

Give each child an assessment sheet. Shuffle the number cards and deal three cards to each child. Tell the children to use the numbers on the cards to answer the questions on the assessment sheet. Assist them with reading the questions and writing their answers if necessary.

Start by asking them to arrange the number cards to make a three-digit number. Ask them to tell you the number they have made, and to write it down in the space provided on the assessment sheet. They should now try to make as many different three-digit numbers as they can with their cards; there will be six different possibilities. The next two questions will give some indication of the child's ability to order numbers according to size.

Question 2 focuses on the skill of rounding numbers to the nearest 10 and 100 and on finding the number 1 less and 1 more than the largest three-digit number they have made.

All six three-digit numbers should be written into the table in question 3 and each one multiplied by 10 and by 100. This will provide some evidence of the children's understanding of place value as well as their ability to multiply three-digit numbers by 10 and 100.

Three-digit number	Estimate	Check
349	3	349 × 3 = 1047

You might want to observe each child more closely as they attempt the final question on the sheet. This asks for an estimate of the whole number by which to multiply each three-digit number so that the product is 1000. For example, if the three-digit number is 349, then the child might decide that 3 would be the best estimate. This is checked on the calculator: 349 × 3 = 1047 and this calculation written in the third column of the table.

The child continues this process with all six of the three-digit numbers.

Reference to photocopiable sheet

Assessment sheet 149 contains questions (to be answered by individual children) concerning the three number cards they have been dealt.

Photocopiable page 106 provides the 0–9 number cards needed for this task. You will need at least one copy of this sheet. Each child will need three number cards.

Number structure

Name _____

Date _____

1. You should have three number cards.
▲ How many different three-digit numbers can you make with your cards?
Write them down here:

▲ Which is the largest number you have made? _____
▲ Write out the numbers in order of size, starting with the smallest:

2. Look at the largest number you have made.
▲ Round it to the nearest 10 _____
▲ Round it to the nearest 100 _____
▲ What number is 1 *less* than your largest number? _____
▲ What number is 1 *more* than your largest number? _____

3. Multiply each of your three-digit numbers by 10, then by 100.

Number	× 10	× 100

4. Look at your list of three-digit numbers from Question 1.
▲ What whole number can you multiply each one by to get close to 1000?
Estimate first, then check using a calculator.

Three-digit number	Estimate	Check

 # EQUIVALENCE OF FRACTIONS

To be able to identify simple equivalent fractions.
To relate the equivalence of simple fractions, decimals and percentages.

†† *Small group of up to four children.*

🕐 *30–45 minutes.*

Previous skills/knowledge needed

The children should have had opportunities to develop their concept of the equivalence of fractions, decimals and percentages.

Key background information

The following activity, based on the card game of 'Rummy', requires the children to find fractions, decimals and percentages which are equivalent. The game can be played by up to four players. To assess this task, observe the game and concentrate on the performance of one or two children.

Preparation

Photocopy sheet 150 twice, either directly or mounted on to card. Cut the sheets into individual 'Equivalent fractions cards'.

Resources needed

A set of 'Equivalent fractions cards', paper, pencil.

What to do

Explain the rules of the game to the children, then observe them while they play.

1. The cards should be shuffled and each child should be dealt five cards. The rest of the pack is placed face down on the table. The top card is turned over and placed beside the pack to begin a face-up pile.

2. The children must collect pairs of cards in which the two fractions are equivalent. Point out to the children that two identical cards cannot be used to make a pair, for example $\frac{1}{2}$ and $\frac{1}{2}$.

3. The children begin by looking at their individual hands of cards and putting together any pairs they can. These cards should be placed in front of them for others to check.

4. The first player begins by picking one card from either the face-up or face-down piles. If this card makes a pair with any of the cards he already has, then the pair is put down. Now the player must discard one of his remaining cards on to the face-up pile.

5. The other players take turns picking up a card, making a pair if they can, and putting a card back. The winner is the first player to put down all her cards.

6. A point is scored by the winner and the game can begin again. The first player to score four points is the overall winner.

Concentrate on one or two children as they play the game. Ensure that you can see the cards they are holding. Note their ability to match equivalent pairs of cards. Are they able to identify when they have a matching pair, for example $\frac{3}{12}$ and 25%, or 0.5 and $\frac{1}{2}$? Watch the children complete the game until there is an overall winner. If possible, keep a record of the matching pairs of cards the targeted child has made. This will give an indication of their knowledge of the equivalent values of fractions, decimals and percentages.

Reference to photocopiable sheet

Photocopiable sheet 150 provides a set of number cards for the activity. Two copies need to be made for the game.

Equivalent fractions cards		
50%	$\frac{1}{4}$	0.75
0.25	0.15	$\frac{3}{10}$
$\frac{3}{15}$	$\frac{3}{12}$	$\frac{10}{50}$
80%	$\frac{1}{5}$	$\frac{8}{10}$
15%	$\frac{1}{2}$	$\frac{3}{4}$
$\frac{6}{8}$	25%	20%
75%	0.5	30%

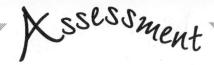

✎ MULTIPLICATION GRIDS

To be able to recall knowledge of multiplication facts to 10 x 10 and use them in the context of a problem. To recognise that multiplication and division are related.

†† *Individuals.*

🕐 *30–40 minutes.*

Key background information

This activity provides an opportunity for summative assessment. It is designed to be completed by individuals, followed by discussion with the teacher. The second assessment sheet can be used to assess children's knowledge of particular multiplication tables chosen by the teacher.

Devise some questions which relate to real-life problems. Can the children give quick answers to these and similar problems? For example:

▲ What will seven pencils cost at 6p each?

▲ How much will it cost to buy five oranges at 9p each?

▲ There are four crayons in a pack. How many crayons in eight packs?

Now ask questions which require them to use the fact that multiplication and division are related:

▲ How many 6p sweets can be bought for 36p?

▲ I have 16 crayons. How many packs of four can I fill?

▲ There are 20 small cakes on a plate and four children sitting around the table. How many cakes can they each have?

Note how quickly the children answer such questions. Determine whether they know the multiplication tables. Do they understand the link between division and multiplication?

4	3	8	7	5
7	1	6	4	2
4	6	9	3	7
3	5	10	7	4
8	1	6	9	8

× [3]

12	9	24	21	15
21	3	18		
12				

Preparation

Photocopy the blank 100 square on photocopiable sheet 120 and amend it to a blank 1–10 multiplication square. Copy this and the assessment sheet on photocopiable page 151 for each child. Before handing out the assessment sheets, fill-in in the boxes the numbers of the multiplication tables to be practised.

Resources needed

A blank multiplication square and a copy of assessment sheet 151 for each child, pencils.

What to do

Ask the children each to complete their multiplication squares as quickly as possible. Note whether they are able to fill in all the squares easily. When the square is complete, ask each child questions such as: What is 8 × 7? 4 × 6? 3 × 9? Can they give you snap answers without having to refer to their squares?

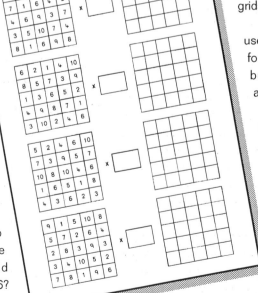

Give each child a copy of photocopiable assessment sheet 151. Ask them to multiply the numbers shown on the grids according to the instructions given. The answers should be written in the corresponding squares on the blank grids (as shown above).

This assessment sheet can be used to reinforce the teacher's own formative assessments and help to build up further evidence of achievement.

Reference to photocopiable sheets.

This activity uses two photocopiable sheets. Photocopiable sheet 120 provides a blank 100 square to be amended into a 1–10 multiplication square.

Photocopiable sheet 151 provides grids containing random numbers which have to be multiplied by a number given by the teacher.

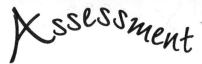

SPECIAL NUMBERS

To be able to recognise some properties of numbers such as odd, even, factors and multiples. To be able to recognise square, triangular and cube numbers.

†† *Individuals.*

🕒 *45 minutes.*

Previous skills/knowledge needed

The children should have had opportunities to explore special numbers such as primes, squares and cubes. They should have had experience of odd and even numbers, factors and multiples.

Key background information

This activity provides an opportunity for summative assessment. It is designed to be completed by individuals. Assist the children with writing their answers if necessary.

Preparation

Photocopy the required number of assessment sheets.

Resources needed

A copy of photocopiable assessment sheet 152 for each child, pencils, calculators (optional).

What to do

Give each child assessment sheet 152. Ask them to look carefully at the numbers in the balloons. Explain that in each box there is one number that does not belong there. Ask them to work out which number it is and why, and then tell them to write their answers underneath each box. Ask them to use their knowledge of special numbers to work out which numbers do not belong. If necessary, do an example with them. Let them use calculators if they wish, to check whether a number is square, cubed, a multiple of 9 and so on.

Discuss the results with them. Ask them to explain to you why the numbers do not belong. Ask them if they can give you another number which would not belong in each set.

Use the completed sheet to determine whether the children have been able to identify the different number properties involved. This can be used to reinforce your own formative

assessments conducted during previous activities on special numbers.

Let the children make some similar special number boxes of their own. This will provide further evidence of their knowledge of special numbers.

Reference to photocopiable sheets

This assessment activity is contained on one photocopiable sheet 152. The answers to the questions on the assessment sheet are: **1.** 15 is not a factor of 36; **2.** 91 is not an even number; **3.** 18 is not a triangular number; **4.** 13 is not a composite number (that is, it is a prime number); **5.** 44 is not a multiple of 9; **6.** 72 is not a square number; **7.** 78 is not a cube number; **8.** 68 is not an odd number; **9.** 22 is not a multiple of 8.

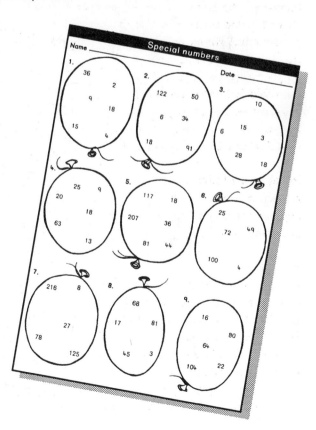

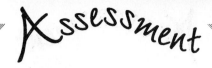
OPERATIONS

To be able to use the four operations confidently. To be able to use a variety of mental methods of computation and choose sequences of them.

†† *Small group of up to four children.*

🕐 *30–45 minutes.*

Previous skills/knowledge needed

The children should be able to use a range of mental and written methods of computation with the four operations.

Key background information

This assessment activity covers several aspects of number; primarily the children's ability and confidence using the operations of addition, subtraction, multiplication and division. To assess this task, observe the game and concentrate on the performance of one or two children.

Preparation

For each group copy photocopiable page 153 directly on to card. Cut the page into individual cards. Write out the following numbers on one or two large sheets of card to that all the children can see these target numbers easily: 360, 174, 295, 347 and 128 (see illustration below).

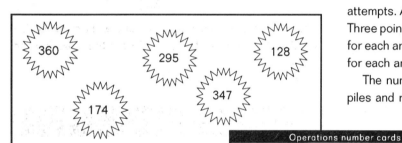

Resources needed

A set of 'Operations number cards' and one or two large sheets of target numbers for the group, paper, pencils.

What to do

Sort the number cards into two sets. One set should contain all the numbers over 10, the other the numbers from 1 to 9. Place the two sets of number cards face down on the table. Give them the sheets of five target numbers to share. Then explain to them how to play the game.

The first player selects six cards in total from the two piles on the table. He should take no less than two cards from any one pile. The six cards are arranged

on the table so that everyone can see them. The object of the game is to use the numbers on the cards to make the first target number. The target can be reached using any of the four operations. Each card number can only be used once, but not all of them need to be used. Each player should try to make the target number, recording their calculations on paper as they go. Each player should aim to make the target number or get as near to it as possible.

For example, if the target number is 360 and the card numbers are 200, 40, 9, 7, 3 and 4; then the target can be reached in a number of different ways.

▲ $40 \times 4 = 160$
$160 + 200 = 360$

▲ $9 \times 4 = 36$ and $7 + 3 = 10$
$36 \times 10 = 360$

▲ $4 - 3 = 1$
$1 + 7 = 8$
$8 \times 9 = 72$ and $200 \div 4 = 5$
$72 \times 5 = 360$

▲ $9 - 7 = 2$
$2 + 4 = 6$
$6 \times 40 = 240$
$3 \times 200 = 600$
$600 - 240 = 360$

▲ $9 \times 40 = 360$

Give the children enough time to work *at least* two attempts. Ask them to compare their results with each other. Three points are scored for each correct attempt, two points for each answer within 5 of the target number, and one point for each answer within 10 of the target number.

The number cards are now returned to their respective piles and reshuffled. Six new number cards are chosen by the next player for the second target number.

The activity continues until all five target numbers have been worked on. The player with the most points is the winner.

Observe one or two children as they work through this activity. Refer to the aspects of number to be assessed.

Discuss with individual children their methods of working. Use the individual child's recording of their calculations as evidence of their ability to use the four operations confidently and accurately.

Reference to photocopiable sheets

Photocopiable page 153 provides a set of number cards for this activity.

Operations number cards		
100	150	50
30	15	10
20	200	40
1	2	3
4	5	6
7	8	9

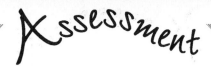

◇ PROBLEMS

To be able to use mathematical reasoning and knowledge to find an answer. To be able to choose an appropriate mathematical operation to solve a problem. To solve problems involving money.

†† *Pairs or small groups.*

⏲ *30–40 minutes.*

Previous skills/knowledge needed
The children should be able to use all the four operations confidently.

Key background information
The solution to the problem is 11. The children will discover that Asha buys 11 crates of drink totalling £44, and 11 boxes of crisps totalling £33. The two amounts add up to £77.

The solution is only one part of this assessment activity. The processes the children use as they try to find the solution should also be noted.

Preparation
Write up the following problem on the board or flipchart beforehand. You may like to prepare a master sheet to copy for each pair, giving the problem so that their ability to transcribe from the board does not limit their performance.

> Asha goes to the supermarket to get some food and drink for the school party.
> A crate of drinks costs £4.
> A box of crisps costs £3.
> She buys the same number of crates of drink as boxes of crisps. Her bill comes to £77. How many boxes of crisps and crates of drink did she buy?

If possible, work through the problem yourself in advance to become familiar with the different approaches that the children might take.

Resources needed
Board or flipchart and marker pen (or a copy of the preprepared problem for each pair), paper, pencils.

What to do
Indicate to the children the problem given on the board (or preprepared sheet). Read it through with them. Then ask them to work together in pairs, and observe them as they tackle the problem. Note how they make a start. Do they try an initial guess at the solution? As they progress, does their approach become more systematic? For example, do they look at possible combinations of prices?

Ask the children to record their work, and provide both a verbal and written explanation of how they tackled the problem.

◇ LEAGUE TABLE

To be able to add together two-digit numbers. To check addition through adding a set of data in a different order. To check addition through grouping data in more convenient sets.

†† *Individuals.*

⏲ *30–40 minutes.*

Previous skills/knowledge needed
The children should be able to add two-digit numbers. They should be aware of different methods for checking answers to addition problems.

Preparation
Make copies of the league table printed on photocopiable sheet 154 for each child. Make yourself familiar with the activity.

Resources needed
A copy of the football league table for each child, pencils, writing materials, calculators.

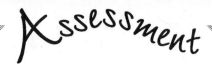

Assessment

What to do

Give the children a copy of the football league table each, and go through the key with them, making sure that they know what the numbers in each column are meant to represent.

Ask them to use the information already provided on the sheet to fill in the missing numbers.

When the table has been completed, ask the children if they can suggest any ways in which the numbers in each column can be checked. Allow them to try any checking suggestions they come up with. Discuss the following ways of checking some of the columns if they have not already been suggested.

▲ The number of games played by a club should equal the number of games won plus the number of games drawn plus the number of games lost:

$$P = W + D + L.$$

▲ The *total* number of games played by all the clubs in the league should equal the *total* number of games won plus the total number of games drawn plus the *total* number of games lost:

$$\text{Column } P = \text{Column } W + \text{Column } D + \text{Column } L.$$

League table	P	W	D	L	F	A	Pts
Blackburn		25	8	5	76	34	83
Man. Utd	38	23		6	70	24	
Nottingham Forest	39		10	9	67	40	70
Liverpool		19	10	8	61	30	
Newcastle	38	19	10		61	41	67
Leeds		17	12	9	52	35	
Tottenham	37	16	11		59	48	59
QPR	38	15	8	15	56	55	53
Wimbledon	38	15	7	16	46	63	
Arsenal	39	13	10	16	50	46	
Southampton		11	15	11	55	58	48
Man. City	38	12		15	50	59	
Sheffield Wed.	39	12	11		45	55	
Chelsea		11	13	14	43	50	46
Coventry	38		13	14	39	56	46
Aston Villa	38	10		15	47	53	
Everton	37	10	13	14	40	48	43
West Ham		11	9	17	38	46	
Crystal Palace	36	10	12		27	36	42
Norwich	39		12	17	34	49	42
Leicester		5	9	25	40	77	
Ipswich	38	6			26	33	86

Key
P Number of games played
W Number of games won
D Number of games drawn
L Number of games lost
F Goals scored by the team
A Goals scored against the team
Pts Total number of points
Three points are scored for each win.
One point is scored for a draw.

▲ The number of points achieved by each team can be checked by looking at the number of games won and drawn. Three points are scored for every win. One point is scored for every draw:

$$\text{Pts} = (W \times 3) + (D \times 1).$$

As the children are adding whole columns of numbers, ask them to estimate the answer first. Question them as to how they add the numbers. Do they find ways of grouping them? Do they round numbers to the nearest 10?

Finally, ask them to check the totals using a calculator. The completed league table can provide evidence of their ability to carry out the necessary calculations. Observing and questioning individual children as they work will tell you the methods they have used for checking their work.

Reference to photocopiable sheet

The football league table on photocopiable sheet 154 provides the data for this activity. The children should fill in the gaps and find ways of checking the figures.

⚽ HANDLING DATA

To be able to represent data appropriately, for example in scaled bar graphs. To interpret graphs with summary statements.

†† Groups of up to six children working individually.

🕐 20–40 minutes.

Key background information

Assessment of this activity will be by outcome. Specific aspects to be assessed include:

▲ Can the children extract and interpret information presented in a simple table? (Evidence from discussion in group, but mainly from one-to-one discussion and from the graph and written work produced.)

▲ Can the children construct scaled bar graphs? (Evidence from graph produced.)

▲ Can they suggest other ways of representing the data? (May provide verbal or written evidence.)

The mode of assessment involves discussing, drawing graphs, writing summaries, giving verbal summaries and explaining the scale used.

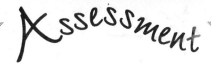

DEPARTURES				
Flight	TO	Time	Remarks	Gate
AF 640	PARIS	09.00	NOW BOARDING	12
PA 432	NEW YORK	09 00	NOW BOARDING	9
LH 049	I IUNICH	09 15		6
KF 250	ALICANTE	09 45		15
JL 054	TOKYO	09 50		3
AZ 350	ROME	09 50		16

Preparation

Copy this table of five different holiday destinations on to the board or a flipchart, or on to a master sheet to photocopy on to card for each child (so that their ability to copy from the board does not limit their performance in the assessment).

Holiday destination	Spain	Italy	Greece	UK	Other
Number	23	6	5	12	14

Resources needed

Board or flipchart, marker pen, or a copy of the destinations table each child, squared or graph paper, pencils, rulers.

What to do

Give each child a copy of the holiday destinations information or indicate it on the board. Help the children to read through the data provided. Spend some time discussing the table:

▲ What is the information about?

▲ How many people stayed in the UK?

▲ How many people went to Spain?

Then ask for suggestions for graphing this information. Tell the children that you want them to construct a scaled bar graph of the data in the table. Help them to realise that they must decide on two things:

▲ what scale to use;

▲ what information to put on the horizontal axis and on the vertical axis.

As they work individually, go around from child to child and ask questions about the scale they are using: What scale are you using? How many will each line stand for? What information is going on the horizontal and vertical axes?

Allow the children time to complete the graph. If they manage this successfully, ask them to write down some summary statements about their graph. These might include:

▲ The most popular destination is Spain.

▲ 20% (or, 12 people) spent their holiday in the UK.

▲ The least popular destination is Greece.

As they write go around from child to child questioning them individually about their graph. Check that they can interpret the results verbally. Ask them how they read a bar graph (that is, the top height of the bar indicates the number of occurrences). Individually, ask them to suggest another graph that could be used to display the same information, for example a block graph or a pie chart. Challenge them to produce another display of the same information. They could use the same or a new scale, if necessary.

Collect all the graphs as evidence of the children's performance.

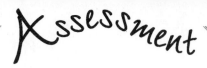

Assessment

PROBABILITY

To know that the probability of an event occurring lies between impossibility and certainty. To be able to use probability language correctly. To be able to order verbal probabilities. To have an understanding of fairness. To be able to test probability through experimentation.

†† *Small group of four children.*

🕐 *20–30 minutes.*

Key background information
This activity is designed to be introduced to a group of up to four children. The probability information underpinning this task is detailed in the probability activities under the heading 'Key background information' in Chapter 4 of this book.

Preparation
Construct two octagonal spinners for each child, one blank and one coloured as illustrated below:

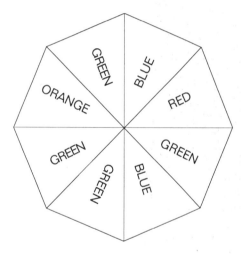

Cut the spinners from card and then pierce the centre of each with a used matchstick with which to spin the spinner.

Resources needed
Octagons of card, used matchsticks, a probability scale drawn on to a sheet of card with the following markings:

0 ——————— $\frac{1}{2}$ ——————— 1

What to do
Give each child in the group a coloured spinner. Then ask them the following questions and encourage them to discuss and justify their answers:
▲ If I spin this coloured spinner, on what colour do you think it would settle?
▲ Why do you say green (for example)?
▲ If I spin it twice, will it land on the same colour both times?
▲ How do you know?
▲ What colour am I unlikely to spin?

▲ What is it most likely/least likely to settle on?
▲ Are you just as likely to spin red and blue?
▲ How do you know?
▲ Is it likely to settle on white? (There is no white.)

Observe whether each child understands and can use the probability language: certain, likely and unlikely.

Now ask each child to pretend that four people are going to play a game with the coloured spinner. Explain that the rules of the game say that the winner will be the person whose colour lands most often. Which colour would each child pick if she wanted to win? Which colours would she not take? Which would be the colour most likely to lose? Would this be a fair game? Why or why not? Finally, ask her to tell you what she would do to make it fair.

Check whether each child understands the notion of a fair game where each player has an equal chance of winning. Give each child a blank spinner and ask them to colour it so that four people could play a fair game. Observe what each child does and then ask them to explain why they coloured it in that way. Check that each child was able to justify her action. Finish up by inviting them to play with the new spinners and test them for fairness. Ask them to say what their conclusions are. Conclusions might include:
▲ Each person had a fair chance of winning as each colour covered the same amount of space on the spinner.
▲ It was a fair game as there were four players each with an equal chance of winning.

Ask the children to indicate the chance of getting certain colours on the spinners using the probability scale. Using the coloured spinner, ask the children what the chance is of getting green. The chance is less than 1 because it is not certain, but it is greater than 0 because it is not impossible. It is $\frac{1}{2}$. It is actually calculated as $\frac{1}{8}$; that is, number of events (which is 1) ÷ the number of possible outcomes (which is 8) gives $\frac{1}{8}$ for each section, and there are four green sections.

Photocopiables

The pages in this section can be photocopied for use in the classroom or school which has purchased this book, and do not need to be declared in any return in respect of any photocopying licence.

They provide a varied selection of pupil worksheets and teacher resource materials. Most of the photocopiable pages are related to individual activities in the book; the name of the activity is indicated at the top of the sheet, together with a page reference indicating where the lesson plan for that activity can be found.

Individual pages are discussed in detail within each lesson plan, accompanied by ideas for adaptation where appropriate – of course, each sheet can be adapted to suit your own needs and those of your class. Sheets can also be coloured, laminated, mounted on to card, enlarged and so on where appropriate.

Pupil worksheets and record sheets have spaces provided for children's names and for noting the date on which each sheet was used. This means that, if so required, they can be included easily within any pupil assessment portfolio.

0–9 number cards

0	1	2
3	4	5
6	7	8
	9	

Big, bigger, biggest

Name _____   Date _____

My number	The highest number I could have made

1.
2.
3.
4.
5.
6.
7.
8.
9.
10.

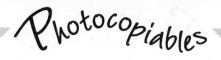

The greatest answer

Name _____   Date _____

Digits chosen   Largest possible sum

1. ☐ ☐ ☐   _____

2. ☐ ☐ ☐   _____

3. ☐ ☐ ☐   _____

4. ☐ ☐ ☐   _____

5. ☐ ☐ ☐ ☐

6. ☐ ☐ ☐ ☐   _____

7. ☐ ☐ ☐ ☐   _____

8. ☐ ☐ ☐ ☐   _____

9. ☐ ☐ ☐ ☐ ☐   _____

10. ☐ ☐ ☐ ☐ ☐   _____

11. ☐ ☐ ☐ ☐ ☐   _____

12. ☐ ☐ ☐ ☐ ☐   _____

▲ What do you notice?_____

_____

_____

Approximating

Name _____ Date _____

▲ Tick the closest approximate answer to these questions.

1.
| 333 + 419 |

640   700   750

2.
| 782 + 349 |

1100   1130   1140

3.
| 3071 − 286 |

2800   2900   2700

4.
| 4431 − 2801 |

1700   1600   1630

5.
| 64 + 128 |

200   210   180

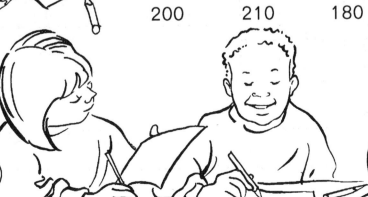

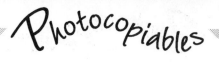

More approximating

Name _____   Date _____

▲ Find an approximate answer to these questions.
▲ Then use a calculator to find the exact answer.
▲ Work out the difference between your approximate answer
and the exact answer.

	Approximate	Exact	Difference
1. 42 × 5			
2. 42 × 51			
3. 163 × 4			
4. 163 × 36			
5. 296 × 99			

Negative numbers game sheet

A shopping spree

Name _____   Date _____

Here are some toys displayed in a shop window:

£4.50
GIANT BOOK of FACTS
£2.50
VIDEO
£8.75
£18.50
£25.99
£16.50
£6.30
£2.45
£39.99

1. Which toy is the cheapest? _____

2. Which toy is the most expensive? _____

3. If you could choose three toys, what would you buy?

▲ _____ ▲ _____ ▲ _____

4. How much would they cost you altogether?

5. If you had £50 to spend, which toys would you buy?

   Are there any other ways you could spend £50?

6. Which *four* toys could you buy for exactly £20?

▲ _____ ▲ _____

▲ _____ ▲ _____

7. How much would it cost to buy *all* the toys in the window?

_____

Piece by piece, page 22

Piece by piece

Game board

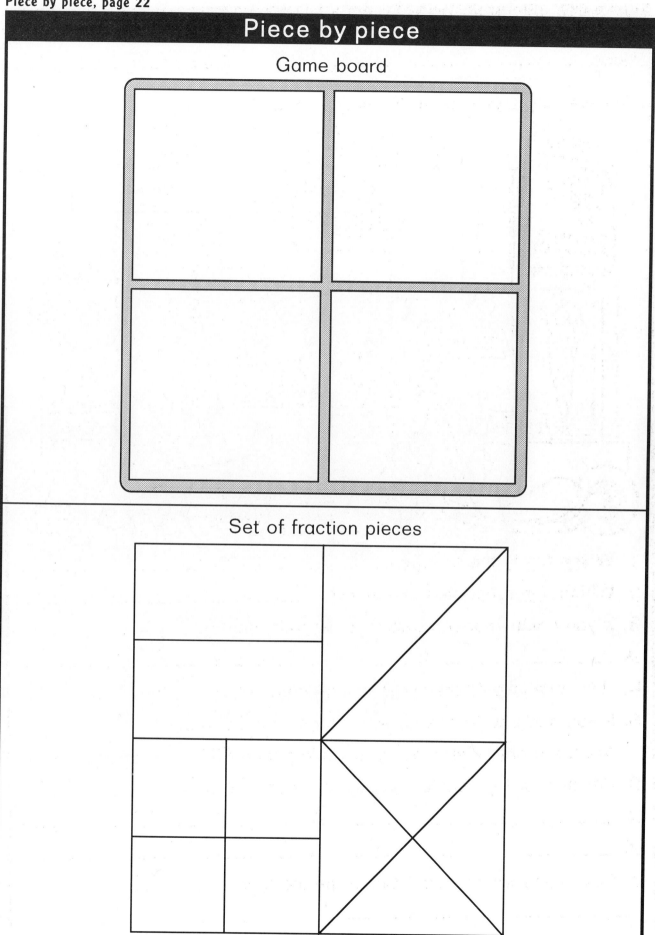

Set of fraction pieces

Fraction families, page 22

Fraction families

Name ______________________ Date ______________

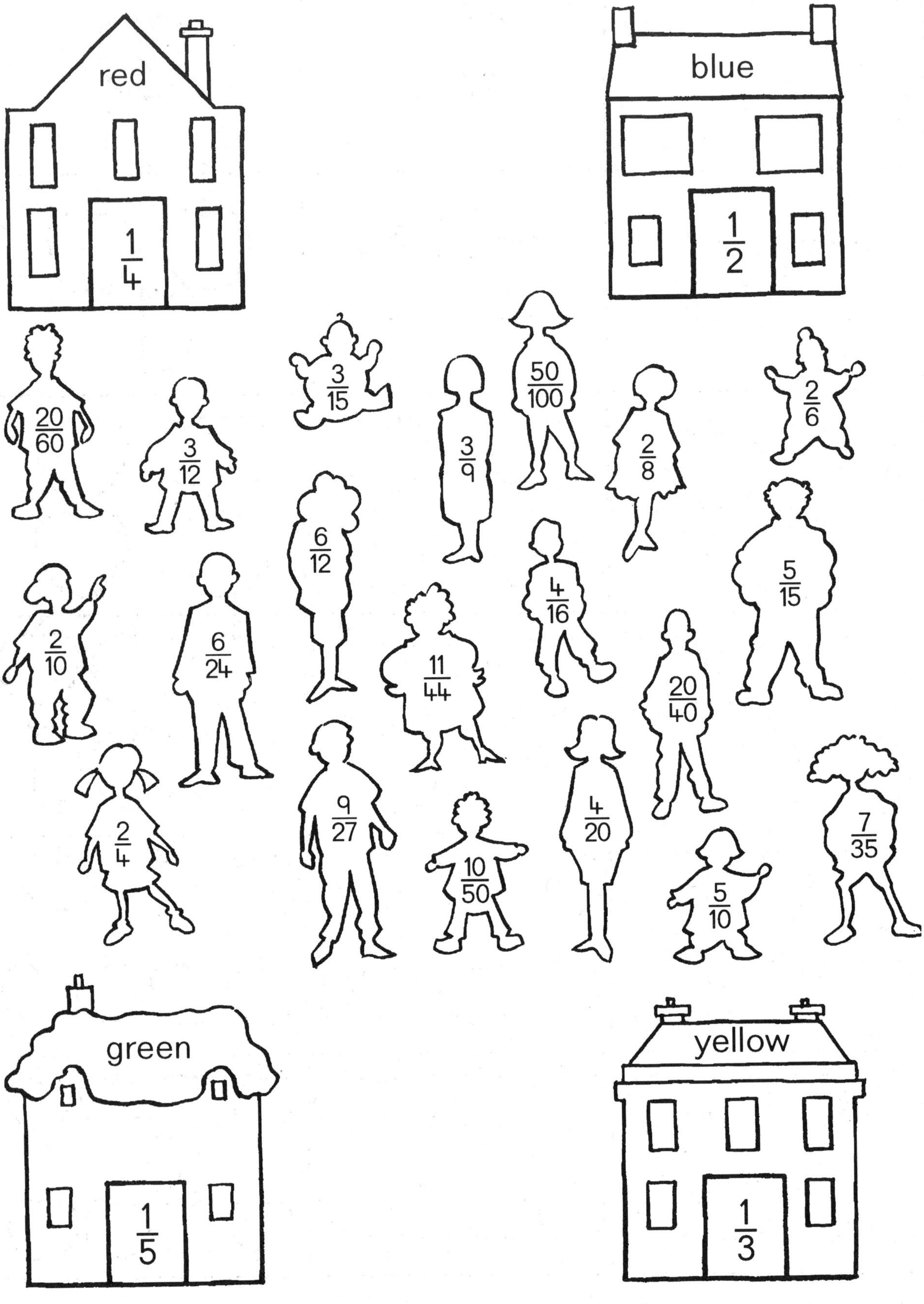
red
1/4
blue
1/2
20/60
3/12
3/15
3/9
50/100
2/8
2/6
6/12
4/16
5/15
2/10
6/24
11/44
20/40
2/4
9/27
10/50
4/20
5/10
7/35
green
1/5
yellow
1/3

Matching fractions – 1

Matching fractions – 2

0	$\frac{1}{2}$	1
$1\frac{1}{2}$	2	$2\frac{1}{2}$
3	$3\frac{1}{2}$	4
$4\frac{1}{2}$	5	$5\frac{1}{2}$
6	$6\frac{1}{2}$	7
$7\frac{1}{2}$	8	$8\frac{1}{2}$

What number am I? page 24

What number am I?

Name _____   Date _____

1.

> 9   12
> 8   7
> 4   6

I am more than $\frac{1}{2}$ of 10,
but less than $\frac{1}{4}$ of 40.
If you multiply me by 2,
I become a $\frac{1}{4}$ of 48.

2.

> 80
> 150
> 42
> 16   75

I am bigger than $\frac{1}{2}$ of 100. I am $\frac{3}{4}$ of a three-digit number with two zeros. If you add 25 to me, you get $\frac{1}{10}$ of 1000.

3.

> 64
> 41
> 30
> 9
> 36
> 28

I am < $\frac{1}{2}$ of 80. $\frac{1}{6}$ of me is an even number. I am > $\frac{1}{2}$ of 60. $\frac{1}{3}$ of me is $\frac{1}{2}$ of 24.

4.

> 4   10
> 20
> 11   23

$\frac{1}{10}$ of me is a single digit number. If you multiply me by 9 you get close to 100. Half of me is $\frac{1}{4}$ of 20.

5.

> 63
> 24
> 81
> 48   3

I am a number less than 50% of 100.
Half of me is a multiple of 12.
Double me and I become $\frac{1}{2}$ of 192.

6.

I am an even, three-digit number.
I am less than $\frac{3}{4}$ of 1000.
If you take away 50 from me, what is left is $\frac{1}{5}$ of 1000.

> 410
> 250
> 356
> 800   103

Fraction of 100

Name _____   Date _____

Look at these two squares. One fifth of each square has been shaded:

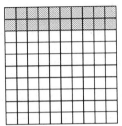 

They show you that $\frac{1}{5}$ is the same as 20 of the small squares, or $\frac{20}{100}$. This can be written as a percentage as 20%

▲ Shade in the squares below and write the fraction as a percentage.

1. Shade in $\frac{3}{10}$ of these squares.

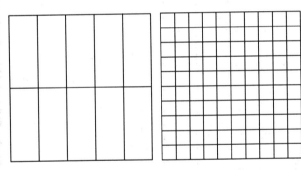

$\frac{3}{10}$ as a percentage is _____ %

3. Shade in $\frac{3}{4}$ of these squares.

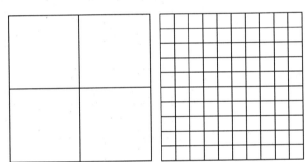

$\frac{3}{4}$ as a percentage is _____ %

2. Shade in $\frac{7}{20}$ of these squares.

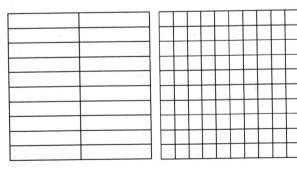

$\frac{7}{20}$ as a percentage is _____ %

4. Shade in $\frac{33}{50}$ of these squares.

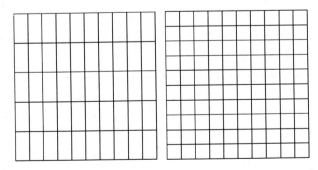

$\frac{33}{50}$ as a percentage is _____ %

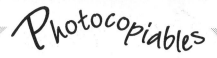

Percentage patterns

Name _____   Date _____

▲ In each of the five squares below draw a simple pattern.
Each pattern should be different.

A ☐   B ☐   C ☐   D ☐   E ☐

▲ Using your patterns, colour in the squares in this '100 square'.

▲ Record the total number of squares that you have used for each pattern.
▲ Work out what fraction of the squares each pattern covers.
▲ Now write each fraction as a percentage.

	Number	Fraction	Percentage
A ☐			
B ☐			
C ☐			
D ☐			
E ☐			

The 100 square, page 28

The 100 square

Name _____   Date _____

Seeing squares

Name _____   Date _____

Grid size	1cm squares	2cm squares	3cm squares	4cm squares	5cm squares	6cm squares
1 × 1						
2 × 2						
3 × 3						
4 × 4						
5 × 5						
6 × 6						

Square magic

Name _____   Date _____

Can you fill in these magic squares? They all have a magic number of 15.

	7	2
		4

	9	
	1	6

4	3	8
	5	

2		
	5	
4		8

6		
	9	4

	1	
	5	
		2

You can use each of the numbers 1, 2, 3, 4, 5, 6, 7, 8 and 9 once only in each square.

Magic number is 15.   → +10 →   Magic number is ☐   → ×3 →   Magic number is ☐

Magic number is 15.   →   Magic number is ☐   →   Magic number is ☐

Magic number is 15.   →   Magic number is ☐   →   Magic number is ☐

Pascal's triangle, page 32

Pascal's triangle

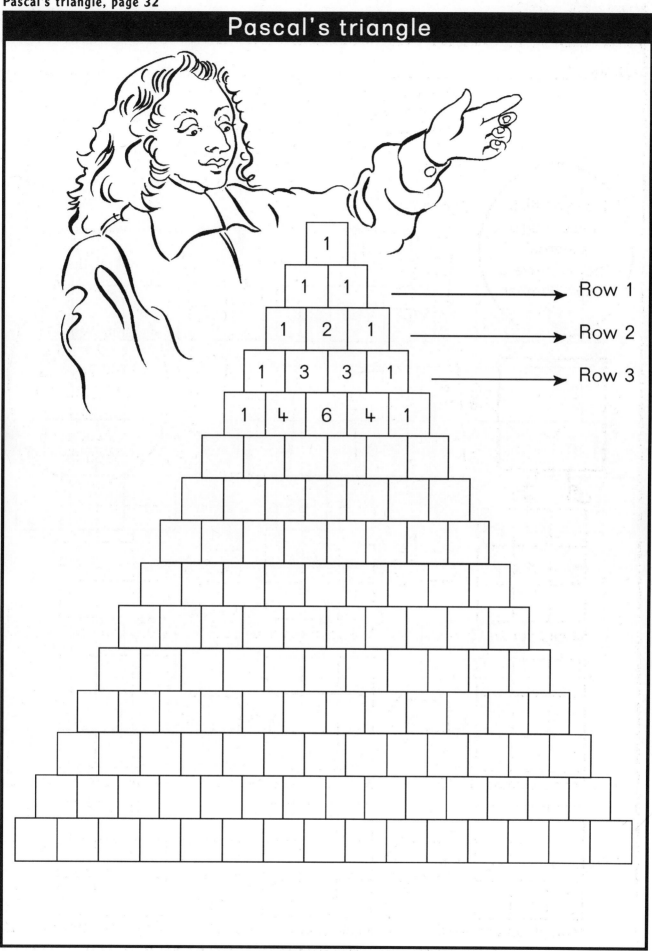

Row 1

Row 2

Row 3

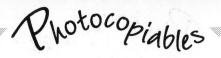
Pascal puzzle

Name _____   **Date** _____

▲ Cut out these pieces of Pascal's triangle.
▲ Fill in the missing numbers and piece them together to remake the triangle.

1

1	1

1		
1	11	55

252		
462	462	330

10	5	1
20		1

84	126
120	
165	

126		36	9
210		45	
165	

| 1 |
| 10 | 1 |
| 55 | 1 |

| 21 | 7 | 1 |
| 56 | | 1 |

| 1 | 9 | 36 |

| 1 |
| 1 | 8 | 28 |

| 1 | 2 |
| 1 |
| 1 | 5 |

| 1 |
| 3 | 3 | 1 |
| 4 | 1 |

| 10 |
| 1 | 6 | 15 |
| 7 | 35 | 35 |
| 56 |

Add and subtract race, page 34

Add and subtract race

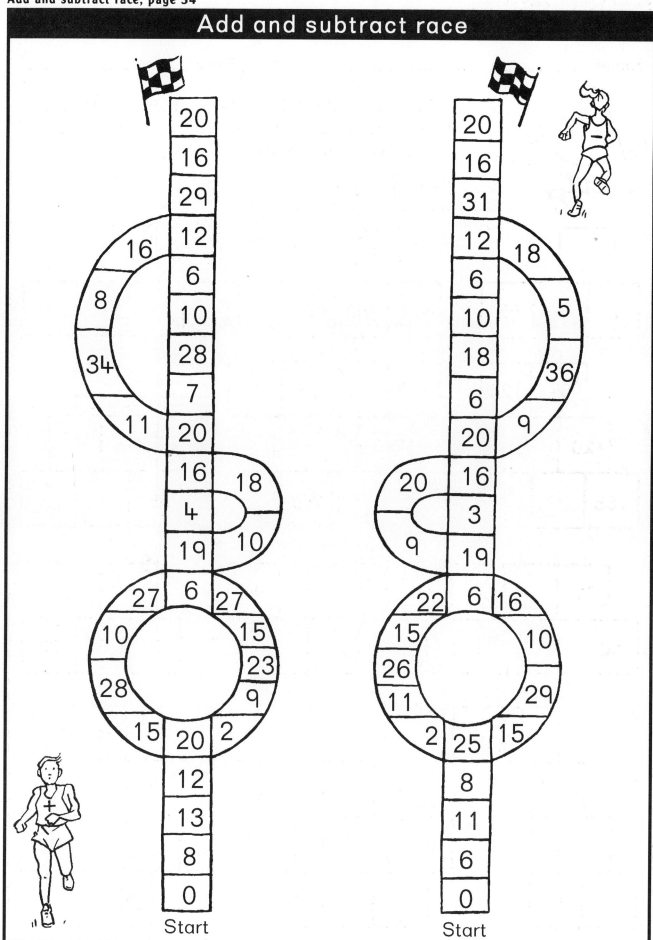

Start

Start

Addition squares, page 35

More addition squares

Name _____   Date _____

▲ Complete these addition squares.

+	2	7
8		
4		

+	6	3
7		
1		

+	6	13
10		
14		

▲ These squares have the answers filled in. Find the questions.

+		
	5	12
	4	11

+		
	10	12
	11	13

+		
	5	7
	6	8

▲ Now complete these squares.

+		
	12	6
	13	

+		
	15	17
	11	

+		
	14	10
	12	

▲ Finally, try this one.

+		
	12	
		12

Cross-numbers

Name _____   Date _____

▲ Here are some cross-number puzzles for you to do.
Use the clues to complete the puzzles.

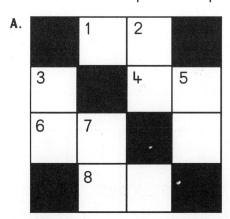

A.

Across
1. 7 + 5
4. 25 + 30
6. 100 – 38
8. 41 – 10

Down
2. 16 + 9
3. 20 – 4
5. 17 + 39
7. 15 + 5 + 3

B.

Across
1. 6 + 14
2. 20 – 4
3. 11 + 11 + 11 + 11
5. 25 – 6

Down
1. 16 + 10
2. 7 + 7
3. 20 + 23
4. 40 – 11

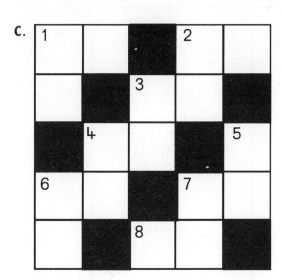

C.

Across
1. 30 – 12
2. 5 + 12
3. 14 + 11
4. 60 – 7
6. 46 – 20
7. 50 + 40
8. 27 – 8

Down
1. 3 + 4 + 3
2. 30 – 15
3. 18 + 5
4. 100 – 44
5. 12 + 28
6. 19 + 9
7. 110 – 11

D.

Across
1. 20 – 9
3. 10 + 28
4. 50 – 4
5. 17 + 17
6. 29 + 21
8. 30 – 13
9. 6 + 8

Down
1. 9 + 9
2. 52 – 26
3. 14 + 16
4. 80 – 36
5. 60 – 30
6. 22 + 35
7. 100 – 16

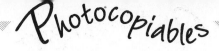

Code capers, page 39

Code capers

Name _____   Date _____

You can use this secret code square to send messages to your friends.

On the square below are some letters. Find the one you want and then write down the number that *should be* in that square. For example, the letter C would be 9 and the letter O would be 100.

So the word 'code' would be 9/100/42/24.

1	G	3	R	5	6	7	8	C	10
11	U	13	14	15	K	17	Y	19	20
L	22	23	E	25	26	27	28	29	30
31	32	33	34	V	N	37	38	39	J
41	D	43	44	45	46	47	48	S	50
51	W	53	54	Q	A	57	58	59	60
61	62	H	F	65	66	67	68	69	70
71	P	73	74	75	76	T	78	79	M
B	82	83	X	85	86	87	88	89	90
Z	92	93	94	95	I	97	98	99	O

▲ What does this message say?
    80/56/77/63/49   96/49   64/12/36

▲ Write a message to a friend. Remember to leave a gap between each word.

Code capers, page 39

More code capers

Name _____   Date _____

You can make your message more difficult to decode by making your friend work out the answer to a sum to find the correct letter in the code square on the 'Code capers' sheet. For example, you could write 7 × 6 instead of 42 for the letter D.

▲ See if you can work out what the following coded messages say. Do each multiplication sum first and find the correct letter in the code square.

1.

12 × 8

7 × 3	10 × 10	5 × 7	12 × 2

9 × 9	50 × 2	25 × 4	8 × 2	7 × 7

2.

11 × 7	21 × 3	8 × 3

10 × 8	50 × 2	6 × 2	7 × 7	6 × 4

2 × 2	8 × 7	6 × 6

4 × 3	8 × 9

7 × 11	9 × 7	3 × 8

3 × 3	3 × 7	20 × 5	9 × 1	4 × 4

3.

40 × 2	12 × 2	8 × 3	11 × 7

20 × 4	4 × 6

28 × 2	8 × 8	7 × 11	2 × 12	4 × 1

7 × 7	3 × 3	7 × 9	50 × 2	10 × 10	7 × 3

▲ Now try writing some messages of your own using multiplication.

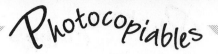

Discover by dividing, page 40

Discover by dividing

You have returned to Lonely Island to recover your buried treasure.

▲ When you reach a circle, work out the division sum and follow the path with the correct answer.

▲ Where is the treasure buried?

Start here.

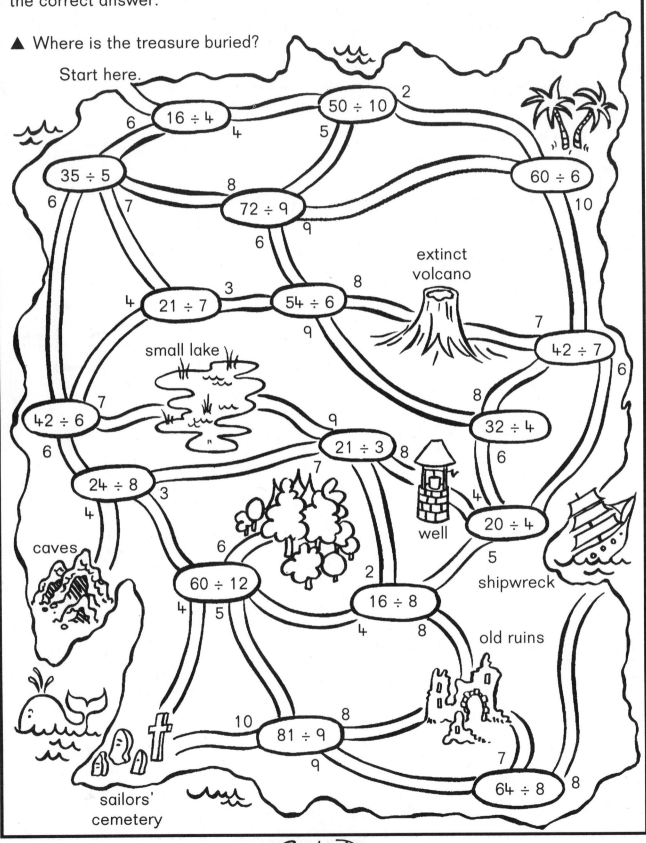

Links of 20, page 41

Links of 20

Names________________________ Date ______________

3 1

15 4

19

17

4 5 8

9

2 10

7

3 18

7 10 5

1

3

6

14 16

3 2 3

4

11 9 1

11

8

2

13 17

7

1 6

2 10

9 and 99 game board

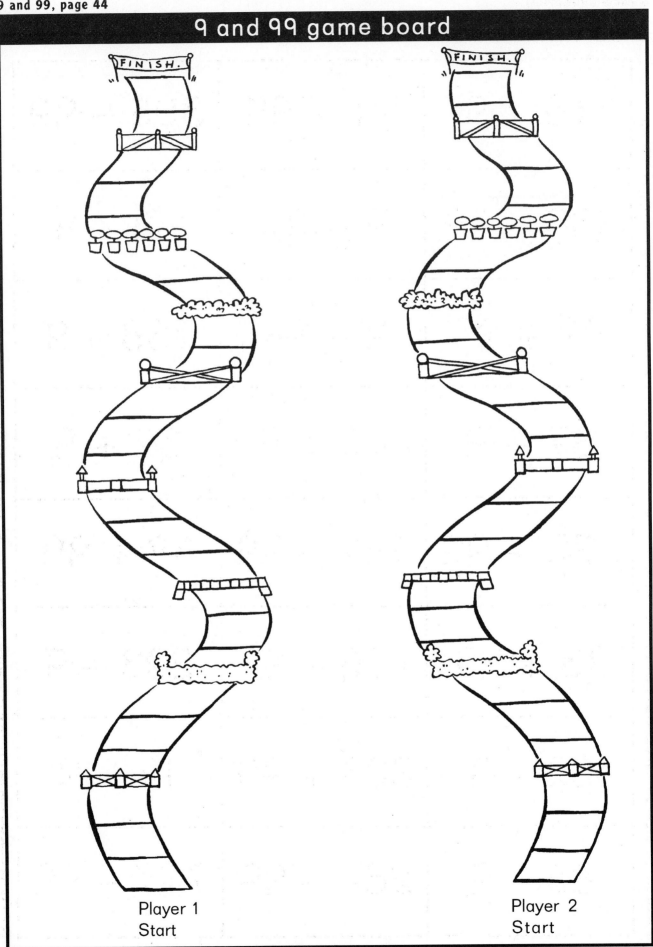

Player 1
Start

Player 2
Start

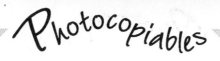

16 + 9	41 + 99	305 – 99
830 – 99	9 + 37	63 – 9
99 + 27	9 + 94	188 – 9
87 + 9	45 + 9	39 + 9
522 + 99	184 – 99	58 + 99
33 + 99	76 – 9	203 – 9
62 – 9	803 + 99	14 – 9
85 – 9	264 – 99	717 – 99

Factor trees

Name _____   Date _____

▲ Fill in the missing numbers:

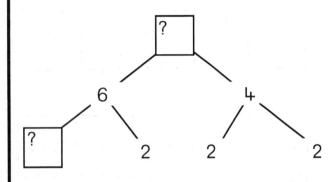

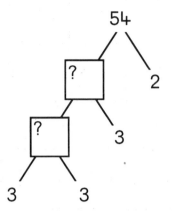

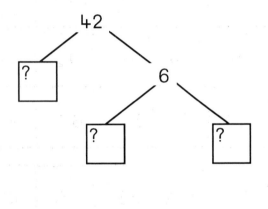

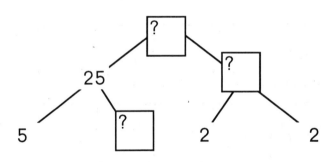

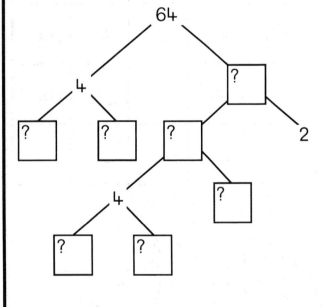

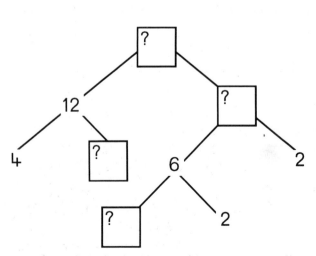

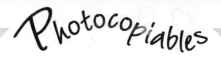
Index bingo

Call numbers

1^2	2^2	3^2	4^2	5^2	6^2	7^2	8^2	9^2	10^2	11^2
1^3	2^3	3^3	4^3	5^3	6^3	7^3	8^3	9^3	10^3	12^2

Bingo cards

1	1000	9	125	49
729	16	27	4	144
36	9	512	25	16
100	1	4	64	8

25	1	8	16	100
64	27	4	216	9
36	100	16	1	49
343	9	729	64	8

144	1	8	81	36
49	64	16	4	729
9	36	25	1	8
121	27	4	16	1000

4	1000	36	216	25
49	343	1	9	144
16	64	8	25	125
36	27	100	4	1

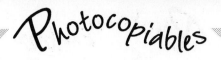
Number properties

Name _____   Date _____

Is it even?				
Is it odd?				
Is it a rectangular number?				
Is it a square number?				
Is it a triangular number?				
Is it a cube number?				
Is it a prime number?				
What are its factors?				
Write down two of its multiples.				

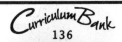

Snake and ladder, page 57

Snake and ladder

Fractions of a number

1	2	3 $\frac{1}{3}$	4	5	6 $\frac{1}{2}$	7	8 $\frac{1}{4}$	9	10 $\frac{1}{5}$
20 $\frac{1}{4}$	19	18 $\frac{1}{3}$	17	16	15 $\frac{1}{3}$	14 $\frac{1}{2}$	13	12	11
21	22 $\frac{1}{2}$	23	24	25 $\frac{1}{5}$	26	27	28 $\frac{1}{4}$	29	30 $\frac{1}{6}$
40 $\frac{1}{5}$	39	38 $\frac{1}{2}$	37	36 $\frac{1}{6}$	35	34	33	32 $\frac{1}{4}$	31
41	42	43	44 $\frac{1}{4}$	45	46 $\frac{1}{2}$	47	48 $\frac{1}{4}$	49	50 $\frac{1}{5}$
60 $\frac{1}{3}$	59	58	57	56 $\frac{1}{2}$	55	54 $\frac{1}{6}$	53	52 $\frac{1}{4}$	51
61	62	63 $\frac{1}{9}$	64 $\frac{1}{8}$	65	66 $\frac{1}{11}$	67	68 $\frac{1}{4}$	69	70 $\frac{1}{10}$
80 $\frac{1}{16}$	79	78 $\frac{1}{2}$	77	76	75 $\frac{1}{15}$	74	73	72 $\frac{1}{2}$	71
81 $\frac{1}{9}$	82	83	84 $\frac{1}{4}$	85	86 $\frac{1}{2}$	87	88 $\frac{1}{4}$	89	90 $\frac{1}{3}$
100	99 $\frac{1}{3}$	98 $\frac{1}{7}$	97	96 $\frac{1}{12}$	95	94 $\frac{1}{2}$	93	92 $\frac{1}{4}$	91

Sale!

Name _____   Date _____

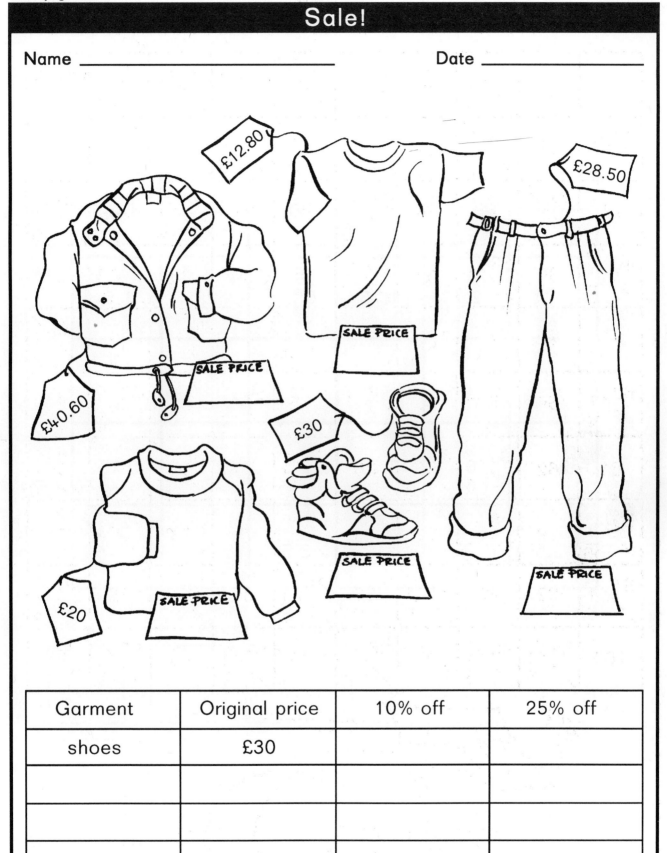

Garment	Original price	10% off	25% off
shoes	£30		

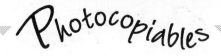

Decimal cover-up

Decimal cover-up game board

2.5	0.25	0.35	1	1.5	0.75
0.9	3	2.25	0.6	1.6	1.85
0.15	2.75	1.75	0.25	2	1.5
2	1.5	1.25	1.15	0.35	0.85
0.25	0.4	3.75	2.5	2.1	0.25
2.5	3	1	3.5	1.4	1

Decimal cover-up game cards

0.1	0.25	0.75	1	1.5	1.75
0.1	0.5	0.75	1.25	1.5	2
0.25	0.5	1	1.25	1.75	2

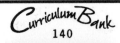

Photocopiables

Target 10

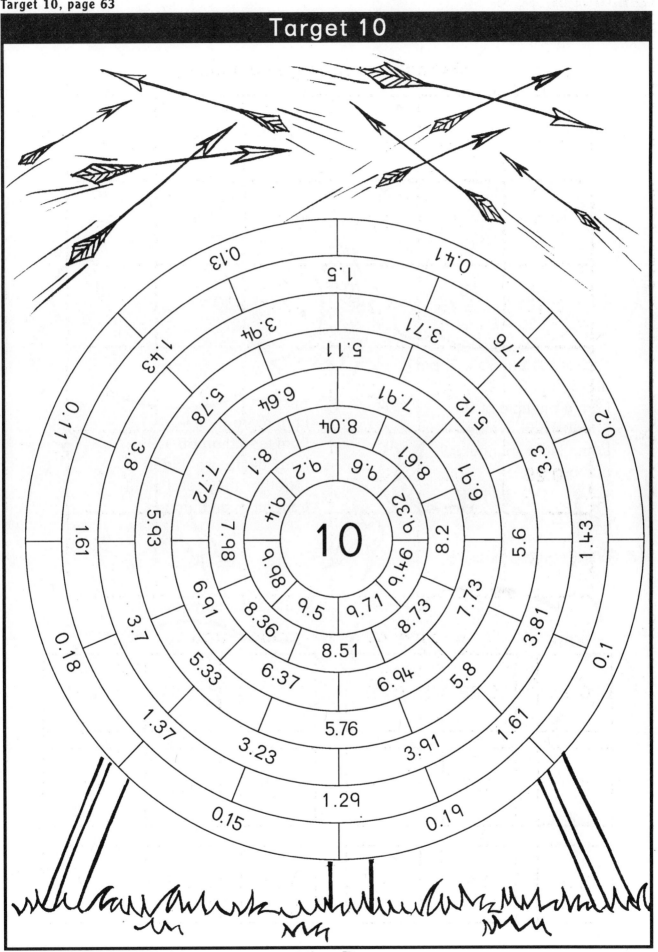

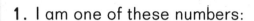

Guess the number

Name _____   Date _____

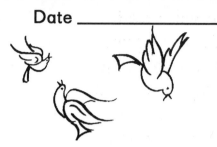

▲ Circle the correct numbers.

1. I am one of these numbers:

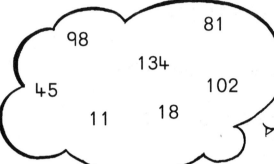

98 81 134 45 102 11 18

I am less than 60 × 2, but more than 6 × 2.
I am a multiple of 9.
I am an odd number.
I am also a triangular number.

2. Which number am I?

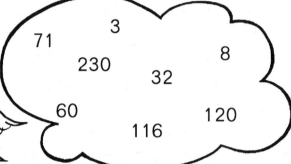

71 3 230 32 8 60 116 120

I am more than 42 + 12.
I am less than 68 + 99.
If my digits are added together they total eight.
I am an even number.

3. What's my number?

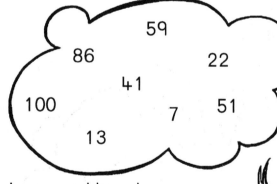

59 86 22 41 100 7 51 13

I am an odd number.
I am less than 7 × 7.
I am more than 110 ÷ 10.
Multiply me by 2 and my product is less than 30.

4. Find the number.

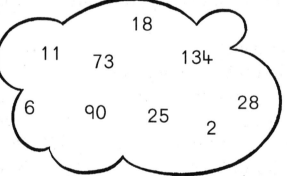

18 11 73 134 6 90 25 28 2

I am an even number.
I am < 6 × 6, but > 6 + 6.
4 is one of my factors.
I am a triangular number.

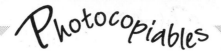
Double the quantity, page 67 and The cost of a biscuit, page 68

Easter biscuits

You will need:

125g margarine
75g caster sugar
1 egg, separated
75g plain flour
25g cornflour

$\frac{1}{2}$ teaspoon ground cinnamon
$\frac{1}{2}$ teaspoon ground ginger
75g wholemeal flour
1 tablespoon milk
50g currants
25g cut mixed peel

What to do

1. Cream the margarine and sugar until light and fluffy.
2. Beat in the egg yolk.
3. Sift the plain flour, cornflour and spices together.
   Work this into the creamed mixture.
4. Add the wholemeal flour.
5. Add the milk to make a dough.
6. Mix in the currants and mixed peel.
7. Roll out the dough (about 5mm thick) and cut into round shapes
   with a 6cm cutter.
8. Put the biscuit shapes on to greased baking sheets.
9. Bake in the oven for 10 minutes at 200°C/400°F/Gas Mark 6.
10. At the end of the cooking time, whisk the egg white.
    Brush this over the biscuits and sprinkle them with some sugar.
11. Put them back into the oven for 5 minutes.
12. Cool the biscuits on a wire rack.

This will make approximately 20 biscuits.

Price list

250g tub of margarine	50p
500g caster sugar	60p
6 eggs	90p
1kg plain flour	£1.00
500g cornflour	40p
1kg wholemeal flour	£1.20
250g currants	£1.25
100g tub of mixed peel	75p

Operations cards

$4 \times ? = 328$	$? \times 12 = 192$	$? \times 15 = 180$	$14 \times ? = 126$	$8 \times ? = 112$	$17 \times ? = 85$	$9 \times ? = 198$
$? \div 11 = 24$	$234 \div ? = 26$	$? \div 10 = 20$	$300 \div ? = 75$	$99 \div ? = 33$	$? \div 5 = 41$	$203 \div ? = 29$
$? \times 50 = 700$	$6 \times ? = 114$	$288 \div ? = 8$	$? \div 9 = 18$	$21 \times ? = 126$	$68 \times ? = 340$	$? \times 26 = 208$

Find the rule

Name _____   Date _____

The first two numbers in each row have been used to make new numbers.
▲ Follow the rules given below to fill in the rest of the table.

	A Add the two numbers together.	**B** Subtract the second number from the first number.	**C** Multiply the two numbers together.	**D** Multiply first number by 2 and add on the second.
3 and 2	5	1	6	8
7 and 3		4		
6 and 1				13
4 and 3	7			
9 and 4			36	
5 and 5		0		
8 and 2				18
10 and 5	15			

▲ Find the rules (A to E) and fill in the rest of the table. Each letter represents a different rule.

	A	**B**	**C**	**D**	**E**
6 and 4	2	24	5	20	100
9 and 3	6		6		
10 and 4		40			140
4 and 2				12	
8 and 6	2		7		
18 and 2					200
6 and 2		12		16	
14 and 10					

Check your route

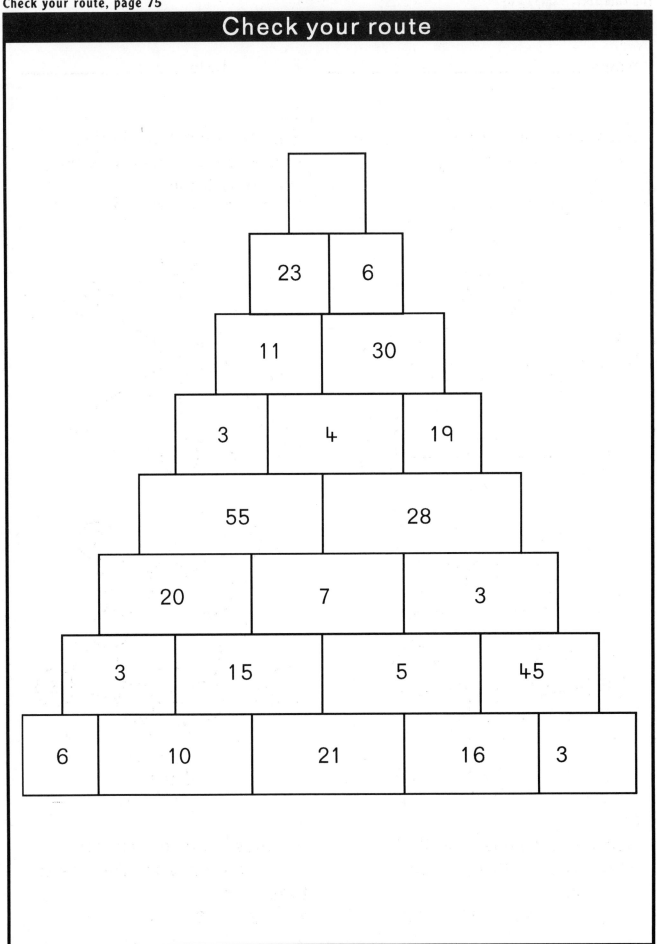

The same total, page 76

The same total

Name _____   Date _____

1.
Put these numbers in the circles to make a magic triangle:

1   2   3   5   6   7

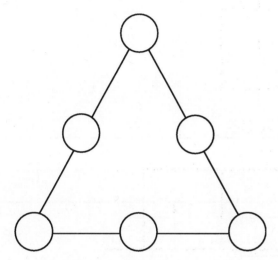

2.
Put these numbers in the circles so that each line has the same total:

1   2   3   5   6   7

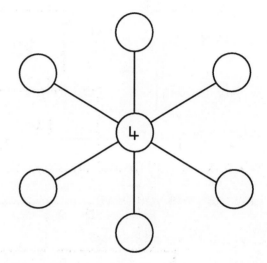

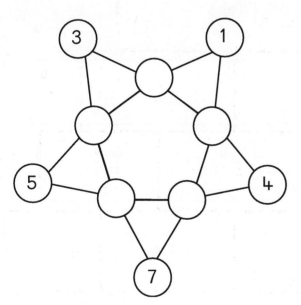

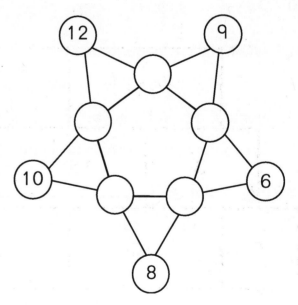

3.
Use these numbers so that all the lines in this star add up to 30:

9   10   11   12   13

4.
Put these numbers in the circles so that each line has a total of 24:

1   2   3   4   5

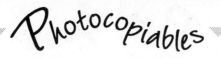

Setting up a database, page 80

Our class

1. What is your name?_____

2. Are you a boy? ☐ Yes ☐ No

3. How many sisters have you got?_____

4. How many brothers have you got? _____

5. ▲ I am ☐ cm tall.

   ▲ My handspan is ☐ cm.

   ▲ My foot is ☐ cm long.

6. What age are you?_____

7. In what month is your birthday?_____

8. List the pets you have:_____

9. Do you have a bicycle? ☐ Yes ☐ No

10. Do you play chess? ☐ Yes ☐ No

11. What is your favourite hobby? _____

12. What is your favourite TV programme? _____

13. Name the best book you read this year: _____

14. Do you play a musical instrument? ☐ Yes ☐ No

15. If so, what is it? _____

16. What subject do you like best in school? _____

17. How do you travel to school? ☐ Walk ☐ Car ☐ Bus ☐ Taxi

18. What is your favourite pop group? _____

19. What is your favourite sport? _____

20. If you have a favourite football team, state it: _____

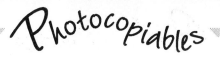

Number structure

Name ——————————————— Date ———————————

1. You should have three number cards.
▲ How many different three-digit numbers can you make with your cards?
Write them down here:

——

▲ Which is the largest number you have made? ——————————————
▲ Write out the numbers in order of size, starting with the smallest:

——

2. Look at the largest number you have made.
▲ Round it to the nearest 10 ——————————————————————
▲ Round it to the nearest 100 ——————————————————————
▲ What number is 1 *less* than your largest number? ———————————
▲ What number is 1 *more* than your largest number? ———————————

3. Multiply each of your three-digit numbers by 10, then by 100.

Number	× 10	× 100

4. Look at your list of three-digit numbers from Question 1.

▲ What whole number can you multiply each one by to get close to 1000?
Estimate first, then check using a calculator.

Three-digit number	Estimate	Check

Equivalent fractions cards

50%	$\dfrac{1}{4}$	0.75
0.25	0.15	$\dfrac{3}{10}$
$\dfrac{3}{15}$	$\dfrac{3}{12}$	$\dfrac{10}{50}$
80%	$\dfrac{1}{5}$	$\dfrac{8}{10}$
15%	$\dfrac{1}{2}$	$\dfrac{3}{4}$
$\dfrac{6}{8}$	25%	20%
75%	0.5	30%

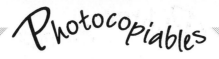

Multiplication grids

Name _____   **Date** _____

4	3	8	7	5
7	1	6	4	2
4	6	9	3	7
3	5	10	7	4
8	1	6	9	8

x ☐

6	2	1	4	10
8	5	7	3	9
1	3	6	5	2
4	9	8	7	1
3	10	2	4	6

x ☐

5	2	4	6	10
7	3	9	5	7
10	8	10	4	6
1	6	5	1	8
4	3	6	2	3

x ☐

9	1	5	10	8
5	7	2	6	4
2	8	3	9	3
3	4	10	5	2
7	8	1	9	6

x ☐

Special numbers

Name _____ Date _____

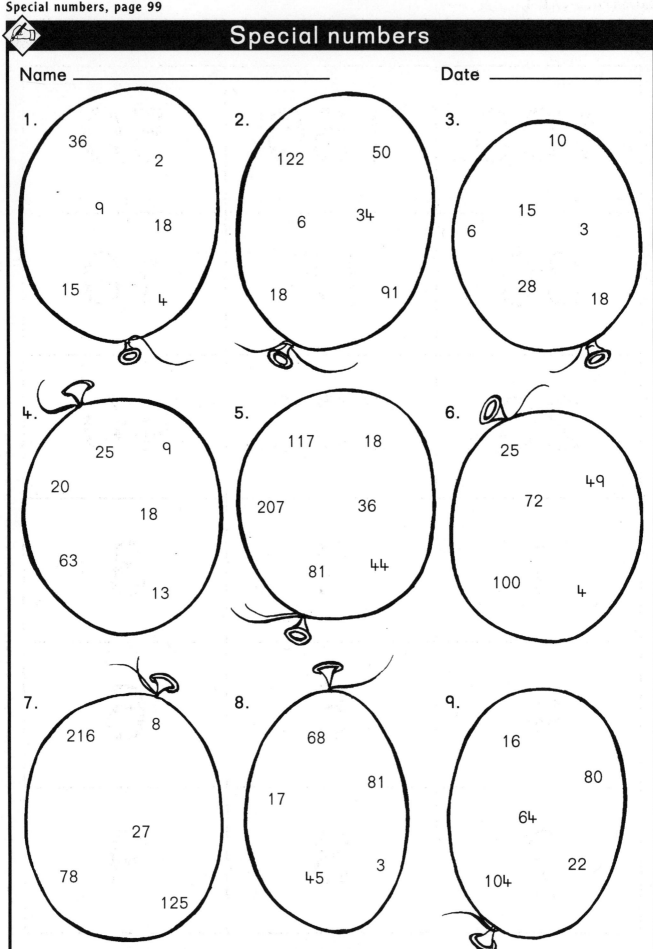

1.
36
2
9
18
15
4

2.
122
50
6
34
18
91

3.
10
15
6
3
28
18

4.
25
9
20
18
63
13

5.
117
18
207
36
81
44

6.
25
49
72
100
4

7.
216
8
27
78
125

8.
68
81
17
3
45

9.
16
80
64
22
104

Operations number cards

100	150	50
30	15	10
20	200	40
1	2	3
4	5	6
7	8	9

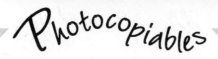
League table

	P	W	D	L	F	A	Pts
Blackburn		25	8	5	76	34	83
Man. Utd	38	23		6	70	24	
Nottingham Forest	39		10	9	67	40	70
Liverpool		19	10	8	61	30	
Newcastle	38	19	10		61	41	67
Leeds		17	12	9	52	35	
Tottenham	37	16	11		59	48	59
QPR	38	15	8	15	56	55	53
Wimbledon	38		7	16	46	63	
Arsenal	39	13	10	16	50	46	
Southampton		11	15	11	55	58	48
Man. City	38	12		15	50	59	
Sheffield Wed.	39	12	11		45	55	
Chelsea		11	13	14	43	50	46
Coventry	38		13	14	39	56	46
Aston Villa	38	10		15	47	53	
Everton	37	10	13	14	40	48	43
West Ham		11	9	17	38	46	
Crystal Palace	36	10	12		27	36	42
Norwich	39		12	17	34	49	42
Leicester		5	9	25	40	77	
Ipswich	38	6		26	33	86	

Key

P   Number of games played

W   Number of games won

D   Number of games drawn

L   Number of games lost

F   Goals scored by the team

A   Goals scored against the team

Pts   Total number of points

Three points are scored for each win.
One point is scored for a draw.

USING AND APPLYING MATHEMATICS

This section of the programme of study should be set in the context of the other sections. It is very important that the children are given opportunities to use and apply mathematics in practical activities, in real-life problems and within mathematics itself. Using and applying mathematics can only occur in relation to the knowledge and understanding of other aspects of the curriculum. It is an approach and not a body of knowledge in itself. Children should be given the opportunity to explain their thinking to support the development of their reasoning. Aspects of the using and applying approach are included within almost all the activities in this book. The table shows where using and applying mathematics can be found in the activities. The asterisks indicate where there may be opportunities for the teacher to incorporate using and applying mathematics in this activities.

The programme of study for using and applying

mathematics is divided into three main sub-sections: making and monitoring decisions to solve problems; Developing mathematical language and communication; and developing mathematical reasoning. Each sub-section is further sub-divided into three or four separate aspects. The headings in the table refer to these in the programme of study. For example 4b refers to 'search for pattern in their results' which is part 'b' of sub-section 4.

The 'using and applying' aspects of the mathematics National Curriculum provide the context within which the content of the curriculum is taught and learned. There has to be a balance between those activities which develop knowledge, skills and understanding, and those which develop the ability to tackle dimension, enable pupils to make use of and communicate their mathematical knowledge, and for many pupils it is the main point in learning mathematics.

The diagram below shows the context, content and proves dimensions of mathematic's teaching.

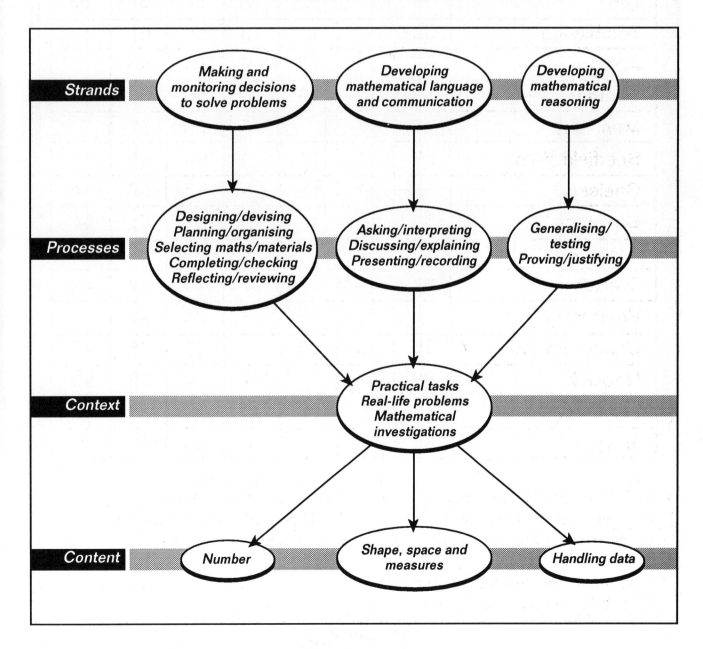

Strands	Making and monitoring decisions to solve problems	Developing mathematical language and communication	Developing mathematical reasoning
Processes	Designing/devising Planning/organising Selecting maths/materials Completing/checking Reflecting/reviewing	Asking/interpreting Discussing/explaining Presenting/recording	Generalising/ testing Proving/justifying
Context		Practical tasks Real-life problems Mathematical investigations	
Content	Number	Shape, space and measures	Handling data

ACTIVITIES	SOLVING PROBLEMS				COMMUNICATION			LOGICAL REASONING			
	Pupils select and use appropriate matter and materials.	Pupils try different approaches; identify and obtain information.	Pupils develop own strategies and look for ways to overcome difficulties.	Pupils check results and consider whether they are reasonable.	Pupils understand and use mathematical language.	Pupils use diagrams, graphs and algebraic symbols.	Pupils present information and results clearly. Explain choice of presentation.	Pupils understand and investigate general statements.	Pupils search for pattern in results.	Pupils make own general statements, based on own evidence.	Pupils explain reasoning.
	a	b	c	d	a	b	c	a	b	c	d
Number structure											
Big, bigger, biggest				●	●		●		●	●	●
The greatest answer	●	●	●	●	●	●			●	●	●
Moving digits	●	●		●	●	●	●		●	●	●
How high can you go?				●	●		●		●	●	●
Approximating	●		●	●	●	●			●	●	●
Negative numbers	●		●	●	●	●			●	●	●
A shopping spree	●	●		●	●	●	●				
Piece by piece	●			●	●	●		●			
Fraction families		●		●	●		●	●	●	●	●
Matching fractions	●			●	●				●	●	●
What number am I?	●		●	●	●		●	●	●	●	●
Fraction of 100	●		●	●	●	●	●		●		●
Percentage patterns	●			●	●	●	●		●	●	●
Number relationships											
The hundred square	●		●	●	●		●		●	●	●
Seeing squares	●			●	●	●	●		●	●	●
Square magic	●	●	●	●	●	●	●		●	●	●
Pascal's triangle	●			●	●	●			●	●	●
Number statements	●	●	●	●	●	●	●			●	●
Add and subtract race	●	●	●	●	●	●					
Addition squares	●			●	●	●	●	●	●	●	●
Cross-numbers	●	●		●	●	●	●		●		
Multiplication square	●	●	●	●	●	●	●		●	●	●
Code capers	●	●	●	●	●	●				●	●
Discover by dividing	●		●	●	●	●		●			
Links of 20	●	●	●		●		●		●		
Adding multiples of 10	●		●	●	●				●	●	●
9 and 99	●		●	●	●	●			●	●	●
Factors	●	●		●	●		●		●	●	●
Factor trees	●		●	●	●		●		●	●	●
Fibonacci numbers	●		●		●	●	●		●	●	●
Sieving out primes	●			●	●	●	●	●	●	●	●
Index notation	●			●	●	●	●				
Number properties	●	●	●	●	●	●	●			●	●

NUMBER

ACTIVITIES	SOLVING PROBLEMS				COMMUNICATION			LOGICAL REASONING			
	Pupils select and use appropriate matter and materials.	Pupils try different approaches; identify and obtain information.	Pupils develop own strategies and look for ways to overcome difficulties.	Pupils check results and consider whether they are reasonable.	Pupils understand and use mathematical language.	Pupils use diagrams, graphs and algebraic symbols.	Pupils present information and results clearly. Explain choice of presentation.	Pupils understand and investigate general statements.	Pupils search for pattern in results.	Pupils make own general statements, based on own evidence.	Pupils explain reasoning.
	a	b	c	d	a	b	c	a	b	c	d
Calculations											
Two for one	●	●	●	●	●	●	●		●		
Snakes and ladders	●	●	●	●	●	●	●	●			
Fractions of a number	●			●	●						●
Sale!	●	●		●	●	●					
Decimal cover up	●			●	●	●					
Target 10	●		●	●	●	●					
Guess the number	●	●			●			●			
Stamps	●			●	●	●	●	●	●	●	
Attendances	●	●		●	●	●	●			●	
Double the quantity	●	●	●	●	●	●	●	●		●	●
The cost of a biscuit	●	●	●	●	●	●	●				
Shopping for the kitchen	●			●	●	●	●				
The school trip	●	●	●	●	●	●	●				
Missing number	●	●	●	●	●	●			●		
Find the rule	●	●	●	●	●	●		●	●	●	●
House numbers										●	
Check your route	●		●	●	●						
The same total	●	●	●	●	●	●	●				
Hidden number	●			●	●	●					
Handling Data											
Setting up a database	●	●		●	●	●	●				
Bar graphs	●	●		●	●	●	●			●	●
Scaled bar graphs	●	●	●	●	●	●	●			●	●
Line graphs	●	●		●	●	●	●			●	●
Mean and range	●	●	●	●	●	●	●	●		●	●
Probability lines		●			●	●	●	●		●	
Probability and prediction	●	●		●	●	●	●	●			
A fair game?			●		●	●	●			●	●
Dicey games	●	●			●	●	●	●	●	●	
Assessment											
Number structure	●	●	●	●	●		●				
Equivalence of fractions	●		●	●	●	●	●				
Multiplication grids	●		●	●	●	●	●				
Special numbers	●	●	●	●	●	●	●	●		●	
Operations	●	●	●	●	●	●	●				
Problems	●	●	●	●	●		●				●
League table	●		●	●	●	●	●				
Handling data	●	●	●	●	●	●	●	●	●	●	
Probability	●			●	●	●	●	●	●	●	●

INFORMATION TECHNOLOGY WITHIN MATHS

There is a vast array of software for use in mathematics and finding a way through it can be confusing and time-consuming. The following ideas may prove useful in evaluating software.

What is the purpose of using the software?

If the software is being used because it fulfils a particular need for a particular child or group then it could be valuable.

Can the content be matched to the child's age and ability?

Can you select options from a sensible choice which are matched to the children's needs? Are they versatile enough to cover a wide range or are they targeted to a single user?

Check that the reading level used within the software is suitable, and that the children can return to the instructions if they need to. Graphical prompts can be more helpful than words, especially for less-able children. Are the questions used in the program 'good' ones. If they are chosen randomly, do the same ones keep reappearing? Can you select the speed at which the questions are asked? If they change too quickly it may not give the child time to respond.

Is the screen presentation well planned?

This may include not only the sequence of the program, but also the way in which graphics or words are used on the screen. Large chunky letters or very small letters may be difficult to read, and the letter shapes may be different from the style used in school.

Colours should provide a strong contrast where there is text to be read, but should not detract the user from the importance of the text. Many of the best software packages allow teachers to alter colours to provide the best conditions.

Where children are asked to move an object around the screen, the speed of the cursor movement in relation to the use of keys or mouse is important. Too fast and the child will overshoot the targets; too slow and the child may become bored. Again, where this is a feature of the program, look for the ability to alter the speed of cursor or mouse movement.

Are the rewards suitable for the child and classroom situation?

Incessant tunes and pretty pictures, which are often used as rewards for correct responses, need to be matched to the children's age and maturity. There is also a need to be able to turn off the sound/pictures, which can become monotonously boring, and even frustrating. However, aural signals can be useful to alert the teacher to a problem.

Some of the best software gives these options to a teacher page which can be preset, and, where a suitable teacher password is used, cannot be altered by the children.

Does the software provide feedback about the child's responses?

Many programs give only a total score at the end of the test, without any direct feedback on the questions that caused problems. Of course, the teacher could sit and watch the responses, but this would be impractical in the busy classroom. However, it is easily within the power of the computer to store all the answers and response times, and even analyse them, to provide direct feedback to the teacher.

Documentation

This varies enormously from program to program. Standards have improved and much documentation now comes with extra ideas for making the best use of the software.

Does the software do the task better than conventional methods?

This is a crucial question. What does the computer offer to this activity that cannot be accomplished by more traditional means? How does using the computer improve the child's learning? If there is no advantage in using a particular piece of software, or if the computer is being used merely because it is there, then the children may be better off without it.

Spreadsheets

A spreadsheet is like a large set of pigeon-holes. Any pigeon-hole (cell) can contain data in the form of text and numbers (or even pictures), or a formula which uses the numbers to calculate an answer which appears in the same cell as the formula. The different cells are referenced by a coordinate system with letters on the x axis and numbers on the y axis:

A	B	C	D	E
1	text	fred	cloudy	brown
2	numbers	100	23.5	–34
3	formula	C2+D2	SUM(C2,E2)	
4			SUM(C3,E3)	

Most spreadsheets contain a set of predetermined formulae which will, for example, add up the numbers in a set of cells or average a set of data. There are also quick ways of replicating a formula down or across the spreadsheet so that the cell references are automatically updated as well. The numbers can be formatted to lie within the centre of a cell, on the right or lined up by the decimal point; the widths of the columns can be changed, and the text styles added to make the results more attractive.

One of the important uses of a spreadsheet is to use a set of data to model a situation, so that if you change the number in one cell it will affect the answer in another, for example, when modelling magic squares.

Most spreadsheets now also contain simple graphing facilities which enable children to plot graphs of one set of data against another.

IT links

The information technology activities outlined in this book can be used to develop and assess children's IT capability as outlined in the National Curriculum. Types of software rather than names of specific programs have been mentioned to enable teachers to use the ideas regardless of the computers used.

Main IT focus

The main emphasis for the development of IT capability within these activities is on modelling and handling information. However, within mathematics there is a wide range of software available to support children's learning and teachers may still want to include specific software which runs on their computer and which addresses the content and understanding of the subject being taught. The activities in this book are very practically based and give children opportunities to use concrete materials and resources to develop mathematical understanding. Content-specific software should not be used to replace such experiences and should be used to develop or reinforce understanding only after initial practical work.

Teachers should also be aware that although such software may assist pupils in their learning of mathematics, it may add little to the development of their pupils' IT capability.

The grids on this page relate the activities in this book to specific areas of IT and to relevant software resources. Activities are referenced by page number rather than by name. (Bold page numbers indicate activities which have expanded IT content.) The software listed is a selection of programs generally available to primary schools, and is not intended as a recommended list. The software featured should be available from most good educational software retailers.

AREA OF IT	TYPE OF SOFTWARE	ACTIVITIES (page nos.)			
		CHAPTER 1	CHAPTER 2	CHAPTER 3	CHAPTER 4
Communicating information	Word processor			64	
Communicating information	DTP			64	
Communicating information	Graphics software		28, 37, 38		
Communicating information	Framework		28		
Information handling	Database				**80**, 84, 85,
Information handling	Graphing software				90, 93, 84, 85
Modelling	Spreadsheet		31, 35, 48	66, **70**, 73	87
Measurement				60	
Control	Calculators	**16**, 17	35		

SOFTWARE TYPE	BBC/MASTER	RISCOS	NIMBUS/186	WINDOWS	MACINTOSH
Word processor	Stylus Folio Promt/Writer	Phases Pendown Desk Top Folio	All Write Write On	My Word Kid Works 2 Creative Writer	Kid Works 2 Easy Works Creative Writer
Framework		My World		My World	
Database	Our Facts Grass Pigeonhole Datashow	DataSweet Find IT	Our Facts Datashow	Sparks Claris Works Information Workshop	Claris Works Easy Works
Graphing software	Grasshopper	Pictogram Picture Point DataSweet	Datagraph Grasshopperx	Datagraph Easy Works	Easy Works
Spreadsheet		DataSweet KeyCount Advantage		Sparks Claris Works Excel Starting Grids	Claris Works
Control	Simple four function calculators				

	ENGLISH	SCIENCE	HISTORY	GEOGRAPHY	D&T	ART	MUSIC	PE
NUMBER SYSTEM AND PLACE VALUE	Telling stories. Writing instructions for their peers and teachers.	Noting similarities and differences in materials when sorting and matching, classifying and counting.	Constructing and using a timeline to sequence events.	Learning about number rhymes from different countries. Finding out about number games and puzzles played around the world.	Design and make board games.	Collecting and sorting images and objects, for example, arranging pebbles in order, e.g. from light to dark (attribute recognition).	Simple counting songs and nursery rhymes, for example *Ten Green Bottles*.	
NUMBER RELATION-SHIPS	Predicting outcomes and discuss possibilities in pattern and sequence work. Predicting what happens in stories such as *Rosie's Walk, The Very Hungry Caterpillar*.	Sequencing events in order, for example life-cycle of a butterfly.	Sequencing events and objects in order.		Designing and making own number puzzles.	Making repeated patterns using potato cuts, sponges, etc. Creating patterns using square, triangular and rectangular numbers. Looking at patterns in art, for example, wallpaper, wrapping paper.	Use musical instruments to make rhythmic patterns. Clapping patterns.	Making up sequence of movements in PE and dance.
CALCULA-TIONS AND PROBLEM SOLVING	Explaining ideas and possibilities in problem-solving. Writing instructions for number games.	Calculating body measurements – handspans, strides. Comparing body measurements for example, height, weight.		Calculate numbers of hours sunshine/rain in last week.	Designing and making items for class shop.	Dot-to-dot pictures.		
HANDLING DATA	Describing events, observations and experiences. Making simple, clear explanations of choices, giving reasons for actions. Writing lists and observations. Reading computer text.	Use drawing, tables and bar charts to present results of science experiments.		Weather observations and recording. Survey of types of homes we live in.	Using computer databases. Using computer to generate charts, graphs and tables.		Favourite pop songs of children in the class.	Frequency tables, for example *How many times can you bounce a ball?*